Essential Guide for
Discrete
Manufacturing
using
Microsoft Dynamics AX

2016 Edition

Other Books by Scott Hamilton

Supply Chain Management Using Microsoft Dynamics AX: 2016 Edition,
Visions, Inc. (2016)

Process Manufacturing Using Microsoft Dynamics AX: 2016 Edition,
Visions, Inc. (2016)

Warehouse Management Using Microsoft Dynamics AX: 2016 Edition,
Visions, Inc. (2016)

Discrete Manufacturing Using Microsoft Dynamics AX 2012,
Visions Inc. (2012)

Food Products Manufacturing Using Microsoft Dynamics AX 2012,
Visions Inc. (2012)

Managing Process Manufacturing Using Microsoft Dynamics AX 2009,
Visions Inc. (2010)

Managing Wholesale Distribution Using Microsoft Dynamics AX 2009,
privately published (2010)

Managing Lean Manufacturing Using Microsoft Dynamics AX 2009,
Visions Inc. (2010)

Managing Your Supply Chain Using Microsoft Dynamics AX 2009,
Printing Arts (2009)

Managing Your Supply Chain Using Microsoft Dynamics AX 4.0,
Printing Arts (2007)

Managing Your Supply Chain Using Microsoft Axapta 3.0, McGraw-Hill (2004)

Managing Your Supply Chain Using Microsoft Navision, McGraw-Hill (2004)

Maximizing Your ERP System, McGraw-Hill (2003)

*Managing Information: How Information Systems Impact Organizational
Strategy* (with Gordon B. Davis), Business One Irwin (1993)

Essential Guide for
Discrete
Manufacturing
using
Microsoft Dynamics AX

2016 Edition

Scott Hamilton, Ph.D.

eBook ISBN 978-0-9973071-3-9
Print ISBN 978-0-9973071-2-2

The front cover photo depicts Kuka robots, and is used permission of KUKA Roboter Gmbh. See www.kuka-robeter.de for more information.

Contents

Preface

This book focuses on how Microsoft Dynamics AX supports supply chain management (SCM) in discrete manufacturing businesses. It covers the essential capabilities and business processes, and presents a linear sequence of topics that build on each other. The targeted reader consists of SCM professionals that need to initially learn AX for manufacturing.

It represents an abbreviated version of my complete book for "Supply Chain Management using Microsoft Dynamics AX: 2016 Edition". It focuses on the manufacturing-related topics, ranging from bill/routing and costing information to master scheduling and production orders. It covers both the basic and advanced approaches to warehouse management for production order picking/receiving.

This book also represents one of a series of Essential Guides for using Dynamics AX in a manufacturing/distribution business. Each Essential Guide covers the most critical capabilities and business processes for initially learning AX.

The book contents cover two major options currently available for using AX, which can be labeled "Dynamics AX 2012 R3" and the "new Dynamics AX". The two options provide the same supply chain management functionality with some slight differences, so that the book contents apply to both options.

Four previous books similarly focused on supply chain management for discrete manufacturing. Each previous book covered a major software version but they could just as easily been titled different editions. The first three books were titled *Managing Your Supply Chain*, and they represented the 2004 Edition (for AX 3.0), the 2007 Edition (for AX 4.0), and the 2009 Edition (for AX 2009). The fourth book was titled slightly differently to indicate the focus on discrete manufacturing, and it represented the 2012 Edition (for AX 2012).

A trail guide and topographic maps provide essential information when exploring any unknown territory. They identify the most important features of the landscape and provide insights about key considerations and trail variations. Similar essentials apply to those exploring the use of an ERP system to run their business. This essential guide identifies the most important features of the embedded conceptual models and business processes related to supply chain management using AX, and provides insights about key considerations and variations.

Many people helped in completing this book. They included Deb Skoog, Elise Kling Marty and Sandra Krzyzaniak in preparing the book. In addition, many people contributed insights and feedback to the previous books which acted as the source material for this simple guide.

The book reflects my interpretation of how to use Microsoft Dynamics AX. Errors of omission and commission, and any misunderstandings, are hopefully minimized.[1] Corrections and suggestions are welcome, as well as additional case study examples. Please send to **ScottHamiltonPhD@aol.com**.

Each day of writing was started with the following prayer:

> Creator of all things, give me a sharp sense of understanding, a retentive memory, and the ability to grasp things correctly and fundamentally. Grant me the talent of being exact in my explanations, and the ability to express myself with thoroughness and charm. Point out the beginning, direct the progress, and help in the completion.

---

[1] The book is for information purposes only. The author, publisher and Microsoft make no warranties, expressed or implied, in the presentation of information.

Chapter 1

Introduction

A primary challenge for many manufacturing firms involves the effective implementation and use of an ERP system for managing their supply chain. Learning the capabilities of your ERP system provides a foundation for effective usage, and re-thinking previous ways of doing business. The learning curve can be shortened with a guide book that covers the most critical topics and processes for running the business. A guide book can help you learn the vocabulary about embedded conceptual models, and enhance the hands-on experience of system usage and navigational details. Each ERP system has its own vocabulary, conceptual models and navigational details, including Microsoft Dynamics AX.[1]

This book focuses on how Dynamics AX supports supply chain management (SCM) in discrete manufacturing businesses. The targeted reader consists of SCM professionals that need to initially learn AX for manufacturing. It provides an overview of the essential business processes and capabilities, and presents a linear sequence of topics that build on each other. It covers the embedded conceptual models that ultimately shape your vocabulary for describing system usage.

As an Essential Guide, it represents an abbreviated version of my complete book for "Supply Chain Management using Microsoft Dynamics AX: 2016 Edition". It focuses on the manufacturing-related topics, ranging from bill/routing and costing information to master scheduling and production orders. It covers both the basic and advanced approaches to warehouse management for production order picking/receiving.

The book contents cover two major options currently available for using AX, which can be labeled "Dynamics AX 2012 R3" and the "new Dynamics AX". The two options provide the same supply chain management functionality with some slight differences, so that the book contents apply to both options.

---

[1] Dynamics AX is a registered trademark of Microsoft. This book employs the term "AX" for short.

This chapter starts with suggestions for the targeted reader, and describes the scope of book topics. It also covers several aspects of terminology and highlights the use of business process modeling (BPM) diagrams as a learning tool. These considerations are reflected in the following sections within this chapter.

1. Suggestions for the Targeted Reader
2. Scope of Book Topics and Prior Research
3. Terminology Used in the Book
4. Variations in the User Experience and the Use of Workspaces
5. Business Process Modeling (BPM) Diagrams as Learning Tools
6. Baseline Model of Operations
7. Summary of Case Studies

1.1 Suggestions for the Targeted Reader

The targeted reader consists of SCM professionals that need to initially learn Dynamics AX for running a discrete manufacturing business. In many cases, they comprise the project team responsible for the initial implementation. In other cases, they may need to learn AX because of a change in positions or job responsibilities. Prospective users (and AX consultants) may also want to initially learn AX for manufacturing. In addition, many people with some AX experience may want to confirm and extend their AX knowledge, or selectively learn a topic. Figure 1.1 summarizes these learning objectives.

Figure 1.1 Suggestions for the Targeted Reader

Learning Objective	Estimated Pages
Initially Learn AX for Discrete Manufacturing	150-180
Extend/Confirm existing AX Knowledge	
Selectively Learn AX for Discrete Manufacturing	
Item and BOM Information	25
Routing Information	30
Product Cost Calculations	30
S&OP and Master Scheduling	20
Basic Warehouse Management for Production	10
Advanced Warehouse Management for Production	20

The objective to initially learn AX for discrete manufacturing can benefit from an overview of the essential business processes and capabilities, especially in a linear sequence of topics that build on each other. The estimated page count of 150-180 pages provides one indicator of the learning effort for the essential manufacturing-related topics within AX.

The linear sequence starts with the definition of a manufactured item, which includes the item's coverage planning data and the policies for serialized or batch-controlled material. The sequence continues with the definition of bills of material and routing information, the calculation of product costs, the common S&OP scenarios, and the use of master scheduling logic to coordinate supply chain activities. Subsequent chapters cover production order processing, and the two major options of a basic and advanced approach to warehouse management for production order picking/receiving. Several quality considerations are also covered. The book chapters reflect this linear sequence, as shown in Figure 1.2.

The book chapters also provide an organizing focus for selective learning of AX capabilities for discrete manufacturing. Different roles may focus on different chapters, such as the roles of a product designer (item and bill of material information), process engineer (routing information), cost accountant (product costing), master scheduler (S&OP), production planner (production orders), and warehouse manager (warehouse management for production). Figure 1.1 indicates the page count for each chapter in order to estimate the learning effort for selective learning.

Figure 1.2 Organization of Book Chapters

Chapter	Foundation Topics	Key Business Processes	Chapter
2	Definition of a Manufactured Item	Production Order Processing	7
3	Bill of Material Information	Basic Warehouse Management for Production Orders	8
4	Resources and Routings		
5	Product Costing for Manufactured Items	Advanced Warehouse Management for Production Orders	9

	Sales & Operations Planning	Additional Topics	
6	S&OP and Master Scheduling	Quality Considerations	10

Many of the chapters start with a basic business process that reflects the key constructs and embedded conceptual models within AX. The typical steps and role responsibilities are illustrated using BPM diagrams. The basic process provides a baseline for explaining key considerations and variations, thereby supporting a "+1" learning approach.

1.2 Scope of Book Topics and Prior Research

This book represents one of a series of Essential Guides for using Dynamics AX in a manufacturing/distribution business, and the scope of book topics was shaped by several factors. This Essential Guide for Discrete Manufacturing focuses on the manufacturing-related topics drawn my complete book "Supply Chain Management using Microsoft Dynamics AX: 2016 Edition", such as bill/routing/costing information and production orders. A separate Essential Guide for Supply Chain Management covered the topics (within the complete book) related to sales, purchasing and transfers, and excluded the manufacturing-related topics. These topics are still applicable to a manufacturer, but this approach helped minimize duplication of topics. It also means that some aspects of the separate guide represent prerequisite reading. Examples include the fundamentals of modeling inventory locations, and explanations of coverage planning codes and inventory blocking approaches.

In addition, this Essential Guide covers both the basic and advanced approaches to warehouse management for production order picking/receiving. These topics were drawn from my complete book "Warehouse Management using Microsoft Dynamics AX: 2016 Edition".

The topics within this Essential Guide were selected to assist SCM professionals initially learn AX for manufacturing, where the topics reflect a subset of software capabilities. More comprehensive explanations about the scope of prior research and book topics are provided in Appendix A.

1.3 Terminology Used in the Book

The terminology associated with many aspects of supply chain management can vary widely between companies and ERP systems. It is often difficult to clearly understand the meaning of a term -- such as inventory status, reservations, shipments, work orders, and sales or purchase agreements -- without a lengthy discussion about its significance.

As much as possible, this book consistently uses the same terminology to describe the conceptual models and software functionality within AX. In most cases, the book's terminology reflects the names employed by the AX software, such as the names of forms and fields. However, it sometimes reflects generally accepted terms or alternative phrasing to clarify understanding.

One difficulty in terminology stems from the book's attempt to explain two different options for using AX, consisting of the AX 2012 R3 version and the new Dynamics AX. The embedded conceptual models and business processes within the two options are fundamentally the same for supply chain management topics, but there are slight changes. A comprehensive list of these changes was not available prior to book publications. The book uses the new term when known, otherwise it uses the terminology from AX 2012 R3.

1.4 Variations in the User Experience and the Use of Workspaces

This book focuses on the embedded conceptual models and business processes within standard AX. The user experience and navigational details may differ -- whether using customized forms, workspaces, web-based applications, or hand-held devices -- but the embedded conceptual models and business processes still apply. This section summarizes the variations in user experience and the use of workspaces.

Variations of the User Experience The standard menu structure and user-defined favorites provide commonly used approaches for navigation. When using the new Dynamics AX, the links within workspaces provide another approach for navigating to commonly used tasks. An additional approach – termed "search for a page" – enables you to specify the desired topic, review a list of applicable forms, and then navigate to a selected form.

Use of Workspaces Workspaces represent one variation in the user experience when using the new Dynamics AX. [2] Workspaces provide an aggregation of tasks related to a specific role. Almost half of the 30+ currently

---

[2] The workspace functionality replaces several capabilities in AX 2012 R3, such as role-centered pages and the employee portal. The role-centered pages were built on the deprecated Enterprise Portal capabilities which have been replaced by the new web client platform. The new platform supports the use of workspaces - and the related definition of workspace patterns to support different devices - for navigating to commonly used tasks. For example, a workspace pattern can be specified for a list page, where the number of displayed columns needs to reflect the size of the device.

available workspaces apply to SCM-related topics. Separate sections within the book identify the workspaces related to item definition (Section 2.8), master scheduling (Section 6.10), and production orders (Section 7.13).

1.5 Business Process Modeling (BPM) Diagrams as a Learning Tool

One of the book's primary objectives consists of learning the embedded conceptual models and business processes within standard AX. In many implementations, these business processes can help the project team gain an overall understanding of system usage and each team member's roles, enabling them to envision new business practices and the real need for customizations. Many of the chapters include Business Process Modeling (BPM) diagrams about basic business processes. These basic processes provide the foundation for more extended explanations and for covering major variations. Figure 1.3 summarizes the examples of basic processes described in the book,

Figure 1.3 Examples of SCM-Related Business Processes

Design	Define a material item Define an item's bill of material Define a production resource Define an item's routing	Produce	Process a production order Report labor using MES capabilities
S&OP	Maintain S&OP game plans - For a make-to-stock product - For a make-to-order product	Warehouse	Use Basic Approach: - Picking for a production order - Receive a production order Use Advanced WMS Approach: - Picking for a production order - Receive a production order
Quality	Production Inspection using a Quality Order		

BPM diagrams are primarily used as a learning tool within this book, and my diagrams do not adhere exactly to the BPM standards. The diagrams employ a limited number of symbols to keep things simple. For example, three symbols are used to denote "And", "Or" and "Any, None, or All". A fourth symbol for an "Event" indicates an automatic action within AX, which helps explain some of the behind-the-scenes functionality. The BPM diagrams indicate a sub-process using a bold border for the activity.

1.6 Baseline Model of Operations

A baseline model of operations represents the common use of Dynamics AX and dominant business practices within many manufacturing businesses. It provides a foundation for simplified explanations about how to use Dynamics AX to manage the business, and for explaining variations to the baseline model. In summary, the baseline model focuses on a single AX company with one or more AX sites (and their related AX warehouses) with standard products identified by an item number. Inventory is tracked by site, warehouse and bin location, with inventory replenishment logic at the site/warehouse level. Sales prices and purchase prices are typically companywide, although they can optionally reflect site- or warehouse-specific prices. Each manufactured item requires bill of material information, with optional definition of routing data. The following points provide more detailed explanations about the baseline model of operations.

Single Company and AX Instance The baseline model consists of a single company using a single AX instance. Some scenarios involve multiple companies within one instance and possible partitioning of these companies within the database. A multicompany supply chain is treated as a variation to the baseline model.

Multiple Inventory Locations Identified by an AX site and AX Warehouse Each physical location is typically identified by an AX site and an associated value for a "site" financial dimension. The site-specific financial dimension supports financial reports by site. Each AX site has one or more AX warehouses. Each AX warehouse has one or more bin locations, although use of bin locations is not mandatory. The definition and use of warehouse locations differ significantly between the basic and advanced approach to warehouse management.

Material Items Identified by Item Number Material items are identified by an item number. In some cases, an item may be identified by an item number and one or more additional fields termed variant codes, as illustrated in Case 3.3. In other cases, a product configurator can result in the creation of a configuration ID for the item number. These are treated as variations to the baseline model of operations.

Bill of Material and Routing for a Manufactured Item A bill of material (BOM) defines the product structure for a manufactured item. Alternatively, the product structure can be defined by a formula, especially in process-oriented operations. Many scenarios will also define production resources and routings for manufactured items, but it is optional.

Standard or Actual Costing for Material Items Each material item must be assigned an inventory valuation method reflecting a standard cost or actual cost method. With standard costing, a costing version must be defined for standard costs, and each material item must have an item cost record for each site with inventory.

Inventory Replenishment Logic Applies to the Site/Warehouse Level Replenishment logic is defined by an item's coverage planning data, and applies to the site/warehouse level. In some cases, the logic may only apply to the site.

Batch and/or Serial Numbers for a Material Item The use of batch and/or serial numbers is treated as a variation to the baseline model.

1.7 Summary of Case Studies

Case studies illustrate how the AX software functionality applies to many different scenarios in discrete manufacturing. Each chapter includes case studies applicable to the topic, and a complete list of case studies is provided at the end of the book. Additional case studies are included in the complete book.

Chapter 2

Definition of a Manufactured Item

Information about material items provides the foundation for managing supply chain activities in manufacturing environments. A comprehensive common database about item information must satisfy requirements stemming from multiple stakeholders to avoid the problems associated with multiple nonintegrated files. The stakeholders include sales, purchasing, warehouse management, quality and accounting, as well as engineering and production for manufactured items. Other stakeholder considerations include customers, vendors, industry standards, intercompany coordination, international operations and web-based applications. The multiple stakeholders often have differing requirements concerning the definition of an item.

This chapter focuses on the definition of manufactured items identified by an item number. In AX terminology, this means you initially define each item by assigning a Product Type of *Item* and a Product Subtype of *Product*, which indicates the item identifier consists of just an item number. In addition, each item must be treated as a stocked product based on a policy within the Item Model Group assigned to the item.

A typical business process to define a material item provides a starting point for further explanation about key aspects of manufactured items. The typical process requires an understanding of enterprise- versus company-level information about an item. Key aspects include policies for serial or batch numbers, the coverage planning data for manufactured items, and support for configure-to-order items. These topics are reflected in the following sections within this chapter.

1. Typical Process to Define a Material Item
2. Additional Information for a Manufactured Item
3. Policies for a Serial- or Batch-Controlled Item
4. Planning Data for Manufactured Items
5. Special Cases of Planning Data
6. Planning Data for Master Schedule Purposes
7. Configurable Items
8. Workspaces Related to Item Definition

2.1 Typical Process to Define a Material Item

The business process for defining a material item requires an understanding of enterprise-level versus company-level information within AX. In summary, the concept of enterprise- versus company-level information has been implemented within AX using two different constructs and their identifiers -- termed the product number and the item number. The product number provides a unique identifier for enterprise-level information about products, whereas the item number provides the unique identifier for company-level information about items. The enterprise-level information consists of just a few key policies and some descriptive information, whereas all other item information is defined at the company level. Two key forms are employed to maintain product and item information: the Products form (for product information) and the Released Products form (for item information).

The conceptual model of enterprise- versus company-level information gives rise to two different approaches for defining a material item, termed the multi-company approach and the single-company approach. Both approaches are included in the typical business process to define a material item. The business process starts with a request for a new item, where a product designer role typically has the responsibility for initially defining the product and item information. The process ends with the approval of the new item.

The typical process to define a material item is illustrated in Figure 3.1. An explanation of each step within the process has been described elsewhere.[1] This section focuses on the unique aspects of defining a manufactured item, as identified by the shaded step within the typical process.

---

[1] The typical process to define a material item was explained in the complete book "Supply Chain Management using Microsoft Dynamics AX: 2016 Edition" and in the related "Essential Guide to Supply Chain Management".

Figure 2.1 Typical Process to Define a Material Item

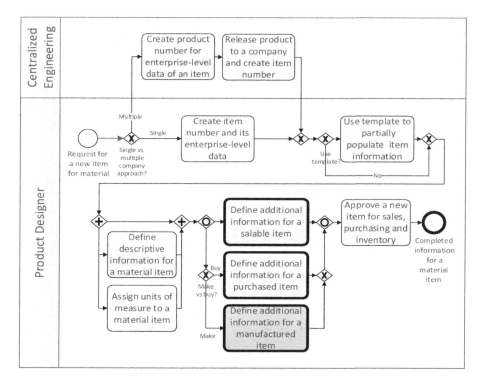

Enterprise-Level Information for a Manufactured Item In addition to the designated Product Type (of *Item*) and Product Subtype (of *Product*), the key aspects of enterprise-level information for a manufactured item include the product number, the product name and extended description (and their translations if applicable), and unit of measure conversions (if applicable).

Define Additional Information for a Manufactured Item The definition of company-level information for a manufactured item involves several activities performed by different roles. The product designer defines an item's bill of material. The process engineer defines the routing for an item. The production planner defines the item's planning data. The accounting manager defines the item's accounting information and inventory valuation method (standard versus actual cost), and the cost accountant calculates the cost of a manufactured item. If applicable, the quality control manager defines the item's testing requirements and the policies for batch and/or serial tracking.

A template may be used to partially populate the information for a manufactured item. However, some aspects of the item information cannot be updated from a template, since they reflect additional tables that must be populated. Examples include the BOM and routing information, the item cost records, the production lead time, and the order quantity modifiers for production orders.

When the manufactured item represents a salable item, the sales manager defines additional information such as sales pricing and possible discounts. The sales manager may also define sales agreements, the applicable product category, and the start dates for selling and shipping a new product.

Essential Data for using a New Item within AX Several company-level policies represent the absolute minimum information in order to use a new item within AX. These policies are termed *essential* item data. The essential data are listed in Figure 2.2 and described below. Two of the policies can be mandated by enterprise-level policies, and two policies only apply to a WMS-enabled item. You can optionally perform a "validation" to determine whether these policies have been specified for an item, and a message displays whether any essential item data is missing.

Figure 2.2 Essential Data for using a New Item

Type of Item Information	Level of Information	
	Enterprise	Company
Item Identifier	Specify Product Number	Inherit Item Number
Product Name	Specify Product Name	N/A
Storage Dimension Group for an Item	Specify as an Enterprise Policy or	Inherit the Enterprise Policy or
Tracking Dimension Group for an Item	Leave Blank	Assign the relevant Dimension Group to Item
Item Model Group	N/A	Assign an Item Model Group to Item
Item Group		Assign an Item Group to Item
For WMS-Enabled Item — Reservation Hierarchy		Assign a Reservation Hierarchy to Item
For WMS-Enabled Item — Unit Sequence Group		Assign a Unit Sequence Group to Item

Legend: ⃕ = Release product to a company when using a multicompany approach to item definition

(Right margin bracket: Essential Information for using a new item within AX)

◆ *Storage Dimension Group for an Item.* The Storage Dimension Group assigned to an item consists of several policies which can be broadly segmented into two groups. One group of policies involves considerations about site, warehouse and bin locations. A second group is related to the basic versus advanced approach to warehouse management, where the policy for "use warehouse management processes" indicates a WMS-enabled item. It works in conjunction with a similar warehouse-related policy that determines the approach to warehouse management.

◆ *Tracking Dimension Group for an Item.* The policies within a Tracking Dimension Group identify the need for tracking batch numbers or serial numbers (or both) for an item. Most multicompany scenarios will assign it to an item at the enterprise level so that it is mandated for all applicable companies. In any case, each company can have a different basis for the assignment of batch numbers or serial numbers. A subsequent section summarizes the significance of the Tracking Dimension Group (Section 2.3).

◆ *Item Model Group.* The Item Model Group assigned to an item consists of multiple policies with a wide variety of impacts. The key policies for a material item include identifying the item as a stocked product and the assignment of an inventory valuation method. The valuation method determines whether actual costing or standard costing applies to an item, and a subsequent chapter provides further explanation of product costing for supporting standard or actual cost items (Chapter 5).

◆ *Item Group.* The applicable G/L accounts are embedded in the Item Group assigned to the item. Additional G/L accounts related to standard cost items must be specified as part of a posting profile.

◆ *Reservation Hierarchy.* A Reservation Hierarchy only applies to a WMS-enabled item, and it indicates how to handle reservation logic at WMS-enabled warehouses. More than one user-defined Reservation Hierarchy may be needed to support the differing reservation logic for normal items versus serialized or batch-controlled items.

◆ *Unit Sequence Group.* A Unit Sequence Group only applies to a WMS-enabled item, and indicates how to handle an item's UM for warehouse management transactions at WMS-enabled warehouses. For example, an item may have three different units of measure (such each, carton and pallet) with applicable UM conversion factors, and the three different UM are defined as part of a Unit Sequence group.

2.2 Additional Information for a Manufactured Item

A manufactured item is typically indicated by its primary source of supply of planned production orders (as part of the item's coverage planning data). An additional policy – termed the Production Type – also indicates a manufactured item. A Production Type of BOM enables you to create a bill of material and production orders for the item, whereas a Production Type of None indicates a purchased item.

The definition of information for a manufactured item involves several activities performed by different roles, such as the product designer, process engineer, production planner, cost accountant and quality manager. Various aspects of defining a manufactured item are summarized below, along with references to more detailed explanations.

◆ Define the bill of material for a manufactured item (Chapter 3)
◆ Define the routing for a manufactured item (Chapter 4)
◆ Define the BOM and routing for a subcontract manufactured item
◆ Calculate standard costs for a manufactured item (Section 5.7)
◆ Calculate planned costs for a manufactured item (Section 5.8)
◆ Define coverage planning data for a manufactured item (Section 2.4)
◆ Define serial or batch tracking policies for a manufactured item (Section 2.3)
◆ Define batch attributes for a batch-controlled item
◆ Define testing requirements for a manufactured item (Section 10.1)

2.3 Policies for a Serial-or Batch-Controlled Item

A user-defined Tracking Dimension Group represents one aspect of the essential information that must be assigned to an item, and it indicates whether serial numbers or batch numbers apply to the item.

Serialized Items   A serialized item is identified by several policies embedded in the Tracking Dimension Group assigned to the item. One policy indicates that each serial number identifies an individual unit.[2]   Additional policies determine whether the serial number assignment must be tracked throughout inventory (the *Active* policy), or deferred until the product is actually sold (the *Active in Sales Process* policy). A second set of policies (termed the Serial Number Group) is

---

[2] Serial number tracking traditionally refers to a unique serial number for each unit of inventory. AX also supports a single serial number for multiple units of an item (conceptually similar to batch number tracking), but this explanation focuses on serial numbers for individual units.

typically assigned to a serialized item that requires inventory tracking. These policies determine whether the serial numbers are assigned manually or automatically. For automatic assignment, the policies indicate the desired serial number mask and when to assign a serial number. It is typically assigned upon arrival which updates inventory balances.

An additional approach to automatic assignment of serial numbers employs an ad hoc serial number mask, which can be defined as part of the item's receipt transaction for purchase orders or production orders. This approach is typically used when serial numbers have already been assigned to the incoming material, and the serial numbers reflect a pattern. For example, the pattern may reflect the same 10 characters and three unique digits in a numerical sequence, so that you could simply identify the fixed characters and a range of numbers to automatically assign the serial numbers.

The Advanced WMS approach involves an additional consideration, since a serialized item must be assigned an appropriate Reservation Hierarchy that includes the serial number. It is typically placed below the location because it is not relevant for reservation logic.

Batch-Controlled Items   A batch-controlled item is identified by a the Tracking Dimension Group assigned to the item, which must include the batch number.[3] A second set of policies (termed the Batch Number Group) is typically assigned to a batch-controlled item. These policies determine whether the batch numbers are assigned manually or automatically. For automatic assignment, the policies indicate the desired batch number mask and when to assign a batch number. It is typically assigned upon arrival which updates inventory balances.

The Advanced WMS approach involves an additional consideration, since a batch-controlled item must be assigned an appropriate Reservation Hierarchy that includes the batch number. The batch number should be placed above the location when it is relevant for reservation logic, otherwise it can be placed below the location when it is not relevant for reservation logic.

Several additional considerations apply to the inventory of a batch-controlled item. This includes vendor batch information, batch attributes, batch disposition codes about restricted usage, shelf life information (for shelf-life items), batch merges, and batch tracking history. These additional considerations fall outside the scope of this essential guide.

---

[3] The term batch number is used because Dynamics AX employs the term lot number as a system-assigned internal identifier for inventory transactions.

2.4 Planning Data for a Manufactured Item

Planned orders communicate the need to replenish an item's inventory, and are generated by master scheduling logic based on an item's coverage planning data and related S&OP game plans. The coverage planning data (or planning data for short) represents a model of decision making about coordinating the supply chain. The planning data differs for purchased items, manufactured items and transfers.

Figure 2.3 summarizes the key planning data for a manufactured item, and highlights the companywide versus site-specific and site/warehouse policies. The information reflects the book's baseline model, where coverage planning applies to the combination of site and warehouse. The bottom of the figure also highlights the four key forms for maintaining an item's planning data. Further explanation covers each aspect of planning data within the figure.

Figure 2.3 Key Planning Data for Manufactured Items

Key Planning Data	Companywide Policies	Site-Specific Policies	Site/Warehouse Policies
BOM Version	Specify BOM as Companywide	Specify BOM as Site-Specific	N/A
Route Version	N/A	Specify Route as Site-Specific	N/A
Primary Source of Supply Planned Order Type = Production	Specify	N/A	Override
Coverage Group (Set of Policies)	Specify	N/A	Override
Production Lead Time	Specify	Override	N/A
Order Quantity Modifiers for Production Orders	Specify	Override	N/A
Planner Responsibility	Specify	N/A	N/A

Form for Data Maintenance: Use Released Products or Default Order Settings   Use Site-Specific Order Settings   Use Item Coverage form

BOM Version The BOM versions for a manufactured item can be site-specific or companywide. Master scheduling logic will use an item's site-specific BOM version (if it exists) based on the site of the item's requirements. If a site-specific BOM version does not exist, master scheduling logic will use the companywide BOM version (if it exists).

Route Version   Master scheduling logic will use an item's site-specific route version (if it exists) based on the site of the item's requirements. The routing data will be used to calculate the lead time for planned and actual production orders, but only within the capacity time fence employed by master scheduling logic.

Primary Source of Supply   A planned order type of Production indicates the primary source of supply for a manufactured item, so that master scheduling logic will generate planned production orders. An item's planned order type (aka default order type) can be specified as a companywide policy, and optionally overridden for a given site/warehouse. For example, a manufactured item may be replenished via production orders at one warehouse, but replenished via transfer orders at a different warehouse.

Coverage Group   The coverage group consists of multiple policies that provide a model of the decision-making logic about coordination of an item's supply chain activities. The policies include the applicable coverage code (such as period lot sizing or min/max) and the use of action messages. More detailed explanation of these policies have been provided elsewhere.[4]   The companywide policy for an item's coverage group can be overridden for a given site/warehouse. As an alternative approach for overriding the coverage group, you can override selected policies such as the coverage code and period lot size.

The capacity time fence determines when routing data should be ignored by the master scheduling logic. For example, routing data may be used for near-term scheduling purposes within the next 30 days, and then ignored after the 30 day time fence so that a fixed lead time applies to the manufactured item.

Production Lead Time   An item's fixed production lead time (expressed in days) can be specified as a companywide value, and optionally overridden as a site-specific or site/warehouse policy. Master scheduling logic will use this fixed lead time when routing data does not exist, or when ignoring the routing data beyond the capacity time fence. In addition, the fixed lead time can be used to determine the due date of safety stock requirements, and to calculate safety stock requirements based on historical usage (Section 10.7).

---

[4] The detailed explanation of coverage group policies was provided in the complete book "Supply Chain Management using Microsoft Dynamics AX: 2016 Edition" and in the related "Essential Guide to Supply Chain Management".

Alternatively, routing data can be used to calculate a variable elapsed time for each production order, where several other factors also impact the calculated time (such as order quantity and capacity availability). The calculated time only applies to production orders within the capacity time fence employed by master scheduling logic.

Order Quantity Modifiers for Production The order quantity modifiers consist of a minimum, maximum and multiple. They are expressed in the item's inventory UM. The order quantity modifiers impact planned production order quantities. They are also considered when manually creating or maintaining a production order for the item, where a soft warning will be displayed when you enter a quantity that does not meet these criteria. The item's standard production order quantity also reflects considerations about these order quantity modifiers, and it acts as a default value when manually creating a production order for the item.

Planner Responsibility The concept of planner responsibility provides an organizing focus for communicating the need to synchronize supplies with demands. The concept of planner responsibility is often based on the production pool and buyer group assigned to a manufactured item. For example, master scheduling logic generates planned production orders identified with the buyer group, so that a planner can selectively view and mark planned orders for which they have responsibility. In addition, production orders inherit the item's production pool thereby enabling the planner to selectively view orders for which they have responsibility. Changes to the order status of production orders can be based on the production pool, and a planner can selectively view action messages by production pool.

2.5 Special Cases of Planning Data

The previous section focused on the planning data for manufactured items, and several special cases require additional considerations. These special cases include phantoms, make-to-order components and buy-to-order components.

Phantoms A manufactured item can be designated as a phantom component in the BOM information of its parent item, where you specify a BOM line type of *Phantom*. Master scheduling logic will calculate requirements for the phantom and ignore its on-hand inventory. Master scheduling logic will also generate a planned order for the phantom, but the planned order cannot be firmed.

Make-to-Order Components A manufactured item can be designated as a make-to-order component in the BOM information of its parent item, where you specify a BOM line type of *Pegged Supply* (or *Vendor*). Master scheduling logic will calculate requirements for a make-to-order component, and even generate planned orders based on the item's planning data.[5] The logic will ignore on-hand inventory for meeting the make-to-order requirements. However, the planned orders simply provide visibility about these requirements, and these planned orders cannot be firmed (for creating a production order). Instead, you automatically create a linked production order for a make-to-order component when you update the status of the parent item's production order, such as updating the status to Estimated or Scheduled. The quantity for the linked production order reflects the parent item's production order quantity and the BOM information about the component quantity. Deleting the parent item's production order will delete the linked production order.

Buy-to-Order Component for Material A purchased item can be designated as a but-to-order component in the BOM information of its parent item, where you specify a BOM line type of Vendor. The preferred vendor for a buy-to-order component can be optionally overridden as part of the component information otherwise it reflects the companywide or site-specific preferred vendor for the item.

Master scheduling logic will calculate requirements for a buy-to-order component, and even generate planned orders based on the item's planning data.[6] The logic ignores on-hand inventory for meeting the buy-to-order requirements. However, the planned orders simply provide visibility about these requirements, and they cannot be firmed for creating a purchase order. Instead, the system will automatically create a linked purchase order for a buy-to-order component when you update the status of the parent item's production order, such as updating the status to Estimated or Scheduled. The quantity for the linked purchase order reflects the production order quantity and the BOM information about the component quantity. Deleting the parent item's production order will delete the linked purchased order.

Buy-to-Order Component for a Subcontracted Service The AX approach to subcontracted production employs a buy-to-order component to represent the subcontracted service. The above explanation also applies to these buy-to-order components.

Purchased Items Requiring Internal Production Some scenarios involve internal production or rework of a purchased item. Internal production may reflect an intermittent basis or a planned change. In this case, the item must be

---

[5] You typically assign a coverage code of Requirement or Period to a manufactured item that has make-to-order requirements.

[6] You typically assign a coverage code of Requirement or Period to a purchased item that has buy-to-order requirements.

designated with a production type of BOM. The item should also have bill of material information to support the use of production orders. When you primarily purchase the item, you assign a planned order type of Purchase Order. You may also need to assign a standard cost reflecting the item's purchase price rather than calculating the item's manufacturing cost. The cost calculations for higher level items should also employ the item's purchase cost, which requires a *stop explosion* policy in the calculation group assigned to the item.

Default Ship-From Location You can optionally specify a default ship-from location for a manufactured item (consisting of a specified site or a specified site/warehouse), and even mandate use of the ship-from location. This approach typically reflects a scenario where the manufactured item is only produced at the specified location. Alternatively, the default ship-from location can be assigned to a customer, typically to indicate shipment from the nearest site when items are produced or stocked at multiple sites.

2.6 Planning Data for Master Schedule Purposes

A master scheduler role is typically responsible for entering and maintaining the S&OP game plans in most manufacturing companies. In most cases, the master scheduler is also responsible for maintaining the planning data for relevant end-items and even stocked components within the S&OP game plans. An additional aspect of planning data involves forecast consumption logic, as defined by several policies within the Coverage Group assigned to these items. Another aspect involves the delivery date control policy assigned to salable items, such as ATP or CTP logic (for make-to-stock and make-to-order products respectively.

2.7 Configurable Items

The nature of custom product manufacturing scenarios often involve a configure-to-order product built from predefined options. Most of these scenarios can benefit from a configuration technology that simplifies the configuration process and embeds engineering expertise. Dynamics AX provides several variations of a configuration technology. The variations are explained within the complete book, and this Essential Guide summarizes one approach.

The primary approach is termed a constraint-based configuration technology, and it requires the definition of a configurable item and a product configuration model. A configurable item is identified as a Product Master within AX (rather than a Product), and requires use of a configuration ID as part of the Product Dimension Group assigned to the item.

A product configuration model provides the dialogue of prompts/responses used in the configuration process, and a mapping of the prompts/responses to the needed components and operations. You can then assign the model to a configurable item along with validity dates.

When using the model, such as configuring a line item for a sales order or a sales quotation, the configuration process results in three key outputs from a supply chain perspective. One output consists of an automatically-created configuration Id for the configurable item. The other two outputs consist of the automatically-created BOM version and route version for the configuration id. These three outputs are also created for each configurable component in a multi-level custom product. You can manually maintain these BOM and route versions, which helps when the configuration process results in partially defined information. Additional aspects of the configuration include a calculated ship date and a calculated cost and sales price.

As the model changes, you define a new model and assign it to the configurable item with different validity dates. You typically duplicate the existing model as the starting point for the new model. Hence, a configurable item will ultimately have different assigned models (aka versions) with non-overlapping validity dates. The configuration process automatically uses the relevant model based on the order date.

2.8 Workspaces Related to Item Definition

Several predefined workspaces are related to item definition, as described in the following summary of each workspace and its applicable functionality.

Released Product Maintenance Workspace This workspace identifies items with a stopped flag for sales, purchasing and/or inventory. Removal of the stopped flags represents an approval step in the typical process to define a material item (Section 2.1). It also identifies recently released products.

Product Readiness for Discrete Manufacturing Workspace The Product Readiness workspace has two variations -- one for discrete manufacturing (using the BOM approach to product structure) and one for process manufacturing (using the Formula approach). Both variations identify items with incomplete information or an expected change. For example, an expected change can reflect a product change case for an item, or an item's BOM version expiring within the lead time for the manufactured item.

Cost Administration Workspace This workspace identifies items with a missing active cost, including standard cost items without an active item cost record.

Product Variant Model Definition Workspace This workspace summarizes several aspects of information about product masters, including the use of predefined variants as part of item identification.

2.9 Additional Case Studies

Case 2.1: Enterprise-Level Policies for Items in a Multicompany Supply Chain A manufacturing/distribution business modeled their multicompany operation using multiple companies within an AX instance, and goods flowed between different AX sites/warehouses in the different companies. As part of the enterprise-level policies for items, they standardized their item identification and product names, the UM conversion factors and NMFC code for each item, and enforcement of batch number tracking. Other company-level policies and data about each item were considered to be the responsibility of each company.

2.10 Executive Summary

This chapter focused on the definition of a manufactured item. Starting with a typical process to define an item, it covered the unique aspects of manufactured items such as BOM/routing information and coverage planning data. It also covered the use of configurable items for custom product manufacturing.

Chapter 3

Bill of Material Information

A key aspect of manufactured items consists of product structure information. The product structure is typically modeled by a bill of material (BOM) in discrete manufacturers. The BOM information defines the product design and provides the basis for product costing, material planning, material usage reporting, batch and serial number tracking, and tracking progress through stages of manufacturing. It often reflects considerations about the routing information, such as the material requirements for specific operations.

Standard products have predefined BOM information, whereas custom products typically involve creation of a unique BOM for a configurable item. This chapter focuses on BOM information for a standard product. The use of a configuration technology to define the BOM for a custom product was summarized in the previous chapter (Section 2.7).

This chapter begins with a typical process for defining an item's bill of material. Key aspects of the business process include the definition of BOM versions and BOM lines, and the maintenance of BOM information. Another key aspect involves the relevant option for defining the warehouse source of components. These considerations are reflected in the following sections within the chapter.

1. Typical Process to Define an Item's Bill of Material
2. Master BOMs and BOM Versions
3. BOM Version Policies for an Item
4. BOM Lines for Components
5. Define the Warehouse Source of Components in BOM/Routing Information
6. Order-Dependent BOM for a Production Order
7. Maintain BOM information
8. Maintain BOM Information using a Product Change Chase

Dynamics AX provides a second approach for modeling product structure information in process manufacturing scenarios. This is termed the Formula approach rather than the BOM approach to product structure. The Formula approach supports several special cases in discrete manufacturing, such as scenarios involving co-products, substitute components or production sequencing considerations. However, further explanation falls outside the book's scope.

3.1 Typical Process to Define an Item's Bill of Material

The typical business process to define an item's bill of material consists of several steps performed by a product designer role. These steps are illustrated in Figure 3.1 and summarized below. As a starting point, the product designer selects the desired item and accesses a separate form in order to create a new BOM version for the item. The new BOM version may involve creation of a new Master BOM or the assignment of an existing Master BOM. The BOM version policies include the effectivity dates. Each BOM line identifies a component and the required quantity. Upon completion of all information, the product designer approves and activates the item's BOM version.

Figure 3.1 Typical Process to Define an Item's Bill of Material

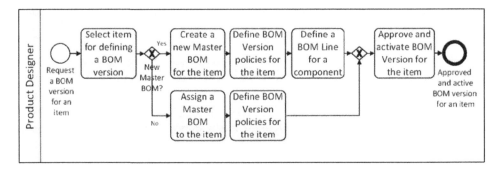

Create a new Master BOM for the Item The creation of a Master BOM typically occurs in the context of creating a new BOM version for a selected item, where the Master BOM is automatically assigned to the item. Each assignment is termed a BOM Version, and an item may have multiple BOM versions, such as different versions that represent site-specific BOMs or planned changes.

Assign an existing Master BOM to the item An existing Master BOM can be assigned to an item, typically reflecting scenarios when the Master BOM has been independently defined beforehand.

Define BOM Version policies The product designer employs the BOM version policies to specify the effectivity dates and to indicate whether the BOM version represents a companywide or site-specific BOM for the item.

Define BOM Line for a Component The product designer uses a BOM line to identify a component and its required quantity. Other considerations include the designated warehouse source of the component, the applicable operation number, and a scrap percentage.

Approve and Activate the BOM Version for the Item The product designer must approve a BOM version before it can be specified for a production order, and an approved version is typically activated for use in planning and costing calculations. Electronic signatures can be optionally employed as part of the approval process.

3.2 Master BOMs and BOM Versions

A master BOM has a unique identifier (termed the *BOM Number*) which can be manually or automatically defined. Manual definition should be used when the identifier needs to be meaningful. The creation of a master BOM typically occurs in the context of creating an item's BOM version, where it is automatically assigned to the item. A master BOM can also be created independently and then assigned to an item. Each assignment of a master BOM to an item is termed a *BOM Version*. A BOM version has several policies indicating the effectivity dates and whether it represents a site-specific or companywide bill of material for the item. Multiple BOM versions can be defined for an item, typically to support the following situations.

◆ Variations between sites producing the same manufactured item
◆ Planned changes with effectivity dates
◆ Revision levels of a manufactured item
◆ Variations that reflect larger production quantities
◆ Alternate bills of material
◆ Prototype or production ramp-up

In summary, a manufactured item can have multiple active BOM versions that reflect different sites, non-overlapping validity periods, and/or different quantity breakpoints. An item can also have approved-but-not-active BOM versions.

An item's BOM version is initially treated as unapproved, which still allows you to calculate the item's costs. It must be approved in order to specify it when creating a production order. Only an approved BOM version can be marked as active. The active BOM version for an item will normally be used in planning and cost calculations.

Electronic signatures can be optionally employed as part of the approval process. For example, you can be prompted for an electronic signature when approving a BOM version, or when designating a BOM version as active. Related situations may also require an electronic signature, such as releasing a production order or reporting the finished quantity for a production order.

3.3 BOM Version Policies for an Item

The BOM version policies serve several different purposes. For example, the policies enable a manufactured item to have multiple active BOM versions that reflect different sites and non-overlapping validity periods. The following explanation covers the key fields in the BOM version for an item.

Site-Specific versus Companywide BOM Versions Specifying a blank site for an item's BOM version indicates a companywide bill of material, whereas a specified site indicates a site-specific bill. The primary difference is that master scheduling logic will use a site-specific BOM version (if it exists) that matches the site of the item's requirements. If a site-specific BOM version does not exist, the master scheduling logic will use the companywide BOM version for the manufactured item. Master scheduling logic will generate an error message if an appropriate BOM version does not exist.

A secondary difference concerns the options for defining the warehouse source of a component. For example, the warehouse source can be manually specified for a site-specific BOM version, but not for a companywide BOM version. A subsequent section provides further explanation about the various options for designating the warehouse source of component inventory.

Effectivity Dates for an Item's BOM Version The effectivity dates for an item's BOM version can represent planned changes in the item's product structure. For example, a manufactured item may have two BOM versions -- one valid to date X and the other valid from date X+1 -- to indicate planned changes. A blank value for the starting and/or ending date indicates no limitation. An item can have multiple active BOM versions with non-overlapping dates.

Quantity Breakpoints for an Item's BOM Version   In discrete manufacturing, the concept of quantity breakpoints does not generally apply to an item's BOM versions although it may apply to an item's route versions. With different route versions reflecting different quantity breakpoints, for example, you can indicate different equipment for producing a larger production order quantity. A planned production order will be assigned the relevant route version based on the required quantity.

3.4 BOM Lines for Components

A BOM line is used to define each component of a manufactured item. Key aspects of a BOM line include the item identifier of the component, the required quantity, the associated operation number, and information about the warehouse source of the component. This section summarizes several key aspects of defining a component, starting with the different approaches to defining component requirements.

Define Component Requirements as a Quantity   The component's required quantity reflects the variable amount needed to produce the parent item. The required quantity also reflects the specified UM for the component. This quantity can be entered as a fraction or decimal. A component's required quantity is normally expressed per a quantity of one parent item, but it can be expressed for a different quantity of the parent item (using the per series field).

Some basic variations to the required quantity include a fixed quantity, the rounding up policy, and planned scrap (expressed as a percentage or a fixed amount or both). A special case of a component's required quantity reflects a non-linear or step-function relationship, but this does not typically apply to discrete manufacturer.

Define the Component's Required Quantity based on Measurement Calculations   A special case of a component's required quantity involves a calculation formula and measurement information, such as height, width, depth and density. This approach often applies to cut-to-size components, such as a cut-to-length component where the component quantity depends on the length measurement of its parent item. In this way, a single master BOM can be assigned to multiple manufactured items and each parent item will have a different measurement for length.

The component's rounding-up policy and multiple take on special significance in this approach. In the just cited example, let's assume the cut-to-length component has an 8-foot length that will be taken from 10-foot steel rod, so that the multiple is 10 and requirements are rounded to increments of 10.

Impact of the Operation Number assigned to a Component   When routing data exists, the operation number assigned to a component provides the key link between the BOM information and the associated operation within the routing.   There are several impacts of assigning an operation number to a component.   For example, the operation's scrap percentage affects component requirements, and the resource assigned to the operation can determine the relevant warehouse source for picking the component for a production order.   These impacts are summarized below.

♦   Align the due date of a component with the start of its associated operation. Components with a blank operation number are required at the start of the production order.

♦   Align the due date of a component with the end of its associated operation, which typically applies to a component representing a subcontracted service.

♦   Calculate component requirements to reflect the scrap percentage of the operation, and its cumulative scrap percentage in a multi-step routing.

♦   Populate the picking list based on the started quantity for a specified operation number (or a range of operation numbers).

♦   Segment the picking list by operation number.   A picking list can be generated for all components with the same operation number.

♦   Determine the resource that requires the component in order to support resource consumption logic about the warehouse source of component inventory.

The operation number assigned to a component should correspond to the operation number in the associated route version for the manufactured item. However, the operation number in the routing may not exist in some cases.   For example, you can specify a different route version when manually creating a production order, or override the operations in the order-dependent routing.

Warehouse Source of a Component   A component's warehouse source indicates where to pick the item for a production order.   There are several options for defining a component's warehouse source using BOM and routing information.   The selected option impacts master scheduling logic about material requirements at the component's warehouse, and the related information will be inherited by the Production BOM and ultimately by the picking list journal for a production order.

As one of the simplest options, you can specify the component's warehouse source as part of the BOM line when using site-specific BOMs. Other options employ the "resource consumption" policy for each BOM line, which defers assignment of a warehouse source until a resource (or resource group) has been scheduled for each routing operation. This requires routing information and operation numbers linking BOM lines to specific operations. The next section provides further explanation about the various options for a component's warehouse source (Section 3.5).

Impact of the BOM Line Type   The BOM line type represents a key policy impacting supply chain management. In most cases, it simply designates whether a manufactured component will be treated as a normal item or a phantom item, as described below. However, it can also designate a make-to-order or buy-to-order component.

◆ *Item (or Normal).* Master scheduling logic will suggest a planned order to satisfy requirements. These orders are not directly linked to the production order for the parent item.

◆ *Phantom.* A phantom only applies to a manufactured item. The requirements for a phantom component are passed (or blow-through) to its components and routing operations. The impact of blow-through logic becomes obvious in the order-dependent BOM and routing for a production order. The netting logic within master scheduling ignores the phantom's on-hand inventory and scheduled receipts (if applicable), and suggests planned orders for the phantom's components to satisfy requirements.

BOM Line Type for a Make-to-Order or Buy-to-Order Component   The BOM line types of *Pegged Supply* and *Vendor* support make-to-order and buy-to-order components, as described below.

◆ *Make-to-order component.* A line type of *pegged supply* applies to a manufactured item, and represents a make-to-order production strategy with direct linkage between production orders. That is, a production order for the parent automatically generates a linked order (termed a *sub-production* or *reference order*) for each manufactured component with a line type of pegged supply. [1] The system indicates linkage via the reference fields in each production order, and linked orders can be scheduled separately or synchronized.

---

[1] The production order for a make-to-order component is automatically generated when the status of the parent item's production order has been changed from created to estimated, or to a higher status such as scheduled.

The netting logic within master scheduling ignores the component's on-hand inventory and scheduled receipts, since the system assumes the component is being produced just for the parent item's production order. The master scheduling logic will generate planned production orders to provide visibility of requirements, but these planned orders cannot be firmed.

♦ *Buy-to-order component.* A line type of *Vendor* applies to a purchased item or service, and it represents a buy-to-order component. That is, a production order for the parent automatically generates a linked purchase order (also termed a reference order) for each purchased component with a line type of vendor.[2] Similar to make-to-order components, the system assumes the component is being purchased just for the parent item's production order, and master scheduling logic ignores the component's on-hand inventory and scheduled receipts. Master scheduling logic will generate planned purchase orders to provide visibility of requirements, but these planned orders cannot be firmed.

A buy-to-order component has one other unique feature, since a preferred vendor can be defined for the component as an override to the preferred vendor for the item. When automatically generating a linked purchase order, the system assigns the component's preferred vendor (if defined) or the item's preferred vendor to the purchase order. This line type is commonly used to support purchases of a component that represents a subcontracted service.

A line type of vendor can also be assigned to a manufactured component, and it works just like the line type of pegged supply. As a minor difference, this type of production order is labeled as *vendor* rather than *standard*. For example, a production order type of vendor could indicate that a subcontractor will produce the manufactured component.

Considerations about Planned Scrap   The planned scrap for a component can be expressed as a percentage or a fixed quantity or both. When using routing data, the planned scrap percentage for an operation can also affect the requirements of components associated with the operation. An accumulated scrap percentage may also apply in a multistep routing because of scrap percentages for previous operations. Each order-dependent BOM and routing (for a production order) inherit the scrap factors from the item's BOM version and route version, and these can be overridden. These scrap factors are included in planning and cost roll-up calculations.

---

[2] The purchase order for a buy-to-order component is automatically generated when the status of the parent item's production order has been changed from created to estimated, or to a higher status such as scheduled.

Effectivity Dates of an Component   The effectivity dates provide one approach for managing planned changes to BOM information, as described in a subsequent section (Section 3.7).

Position Information for a Component   A component's position information provides reference data that can serve different purposes.   For example, it can represent a sequential counter of components, often tied to the find number on drawings.   It can identify a grouping of components, such as the material needed for an operation (when routing data does not exist), the delivery area for a group of picked components, or a group representing related parts in the production process.   The position field also provides one approach for handling reference designators.

3.5 Define the Warehouse Source of Components in BOM/Routing Information

A component's warehouse source indicates where to pick the item for a production order.   There are several options for defining a component's warehouse source using BOM and routing information.   The selected option impacts master scheduling logic about material requirements at the component's warehouse, and the related information will be inherited by the Production BOM and ultimately by the picking list journal for a production order.   This inherited information can be optionally overridden.

Three basic options are summarized in Figure 3.2 and explained below.   These three options reflect the use of a picking list journal for reporting the picked material, which also indicates actual material usage for the production order.   Each option involves considerations about BOM and routing information, and the requirements for additional information vary by option.

The fourth option displayed in Figure 3.2 represents a slightly different purpose for the picking list journal, and it must be employed when using the advanced approach to warehouse management.   It assumes components will be picked and delivered to a production input location based on work orders for Raw Material Picking, so that the picking list journal is only used for reporting actual material usage from the production input location.

Figure 3.2 Variations in Warehouse Source of Components

Purpose of Picking List Journal		Pick from Locations in Suggested Warehouse Source of Components			Pick from Production Input Location
		Option #1	Option #2	Option #3	Option #4
		Use specified warehouse on BOM Line for component	Use default warehouse for item	Assign input warehouse based on production unit and scheduled resource	Assign production input location based on scheduled resource
BOM & Route		Site-Specific BOM	Applies to Site-Specific or Companywide BOM		
		Routing Information not Required	Routing Information Required		
Additional Information		BOM Line has no Resource Consumption Policy		BOM Line has Resource Consumption Policy and an Operation Number linked to Routing	
		None	Item's default inventory warehouse for required site	Resource group has an assigned production unit (with its input warehouse)	Resource group (or resource) has an assigned production input location

Legend: ☐ = Supports the Advanced WMS approach to warehouse management

Option #1: Use the specified warehouse on the BOM line for the component The first option only applies to a site-specific BOM version, and the specified warehouse must belong to the site. After creating a production order for the manufactured item, the component in the Production BOM inherits the component's specified warehouse.

Option #2: Use the default warehouse for the item The second option does not specify a component warehouse on the BOM line, and requires additional information about the item's default inventory warehouse for each site (as defined in the item's site-specific order settings). After creating a production order, the component in the Production BOM inherits the component's default inventory warehouse for the required site.

A shown in the figure, the first two options do not require routing information, and they represent the most straight-forward approach. In addition, they do not employ the "resource consumption" policy on a BOM line, even when routing information has been defined.

Option #3: Automatically assign an input warehouse based on the scheduled resource and its related production unit The third option requires routing information and operation numbers linking BOM lines to specific operations. It employs the "resource consumption" policy for each BOM line, which defers assignment of a warehouse source until a resource (or resource group) has been scheduled for each routing operation. A resource group has an assigned production unit, which might be assigned to multiple resource groups with a common warehouse source of components. This is termed the input warehouse for a production unit. After scheduling a production order, the component in the Production BOM inherits the input warehouse associated with the resource group performing the operation.

Option #4: Automatically assign a production input location based on the scheduled resource The fourth option represents a different purpose for the picking list journal, as mentioned earlier. It assumes components will be delivered to a production input location which will be identified on the picking list journal for reporting actual material usage from the location. Delivering components to a production input location involves work orders for Raw Material Picking when using the Advanced WMS approach to warehouse management. It involves transfer journals or withdrawal kanbans when using the basic approach to warehouse management.

The fourth option requires routing information and operation numbers linking BOM lines to specific operations, and it also employs the "resource consumption" policy for each BOM line, just like the third option.

You define a location representing each production input location within a warehouse, so that it can be assigned to a resource group or to individual resources within the group. After scheduling a production order, the component in the Production BOM inherits the production input location associated with the resource group (or resource) performing the operation.

It is feasible to assign both a production input location and a production unit to a resource group, but the former will be used by scheduling logic for assigning the location to components in the Production BOM.

3.6 Order-Dependent BOM for a Production Order

An order-dependent BOM (aka Production BOM) refers to the BOM lines attached to a production order. It initially contains the BOM lines inherited from the BOM version used to create the production order. Changes to the order-dependent BOM do not affect the Master BOM. Creation and maintenance of the order-dependent BOM reflect several rules.

◆ Creation of a production order for a manufactured item also creates an order-dependent BOM.

◆ The order-dependent BOM initially reflects the item's BOM version that was used to create the production order. In most cases, this will be inherited from the active BOM version for the delivery date and site on the production order. However, you can manually specify a different BOM version for the item when creating the production order, where the BOM version can be approved-but-not-active.

◆ The order-dependent BOM contains components of a phantom.

◆ You can modify the components in an order-dependent BOM at any time prior to reporting the production order as Ended. For example, you can manually maintain the information, or copy BOM lines from another production order or Master BOM.

◆ A material item can be issued to a started production order even when the component does not exist on the order-dependent BOM. The issued component will be automatically added to the order-dependent BOM with a zero required quantity.

3.7 Maintain BOM Information

The maintenance of BOM information can serve different purposes such as planned changes, and several different approaches can be used. For example, you can directly maintain components in a Master BOM, update the BOM components using the copy function or the mass change function, or employ the graphical design tool within AX. This section covers the maintenance of BOM information, and also different types of analysis tools such as multi-level and where-used inquiries. An alternative approach to maintaining BOM information involves the use of product changes cases, as described in the next section.

Manage Planned BOM Changes using Effectivity Dates   Planned changes to an item's BOM can be managed by (1) the date effectivities for a component or (2) by date effectivities for a BOM version. Figure 3.3 illustrates these two options for managing planned changes, and the starting point of the original BOM. The figure reflects a simplistic bill of material to illustrate the options.

Figure 3.3 Manage Planned Changes to BOM Information

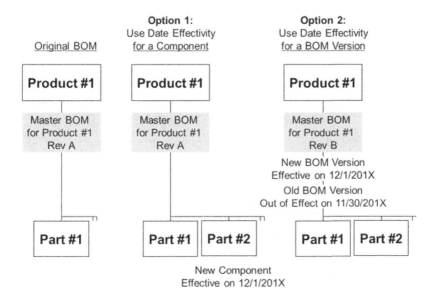

♦ *Option 1: Use Date Effectivity for a Component.* The first option employs date effectivities for a component. The example shown in the left side of Figure 3.3 illustrates the original BOM for Product #1 with a single BOM version (labeled Rev A) with a single component of Part #1. As shown in the example, a new component Part #2 can be added to the BOM version with a specified effectivity date such as 12/1/201X. A component can also be phased out on a specified date.

♦ *Option 2: Use Date Effectivity for a BOM Version.* The second option employs date effectivities for a BOM version. Using the example shown in the right side of Figure 3.3, a different Master BOM can be assigned to Product #1 that represents a different revision level (labeled Rev B versus the original Rev A). As shown in the example, you would phase out the assignment of the original Master BOM on the day prior to 12/1/201X, and phase in the assignment of the new Master BOM on 12/1/201X. The new Master BOM contains both Part #1 and Part #2. The approval status and active status for a BOM version provide an additional consideration for planned changes. Removing the approval status or the active status on a BOM version, or phasing out the effectivity date, provides a selective approach to discontinued use.

A third approach to managing planned changes represents a special case, and generally applies to make-to-order custom products. As part of the BOM line information, it employs a specified BOM version for a manufactured component, where the item's BOM version is approved but not necessarily active. This third approach can build on the use of component date effectivities to phase in and phase out specified BOM versions for a manufactured component.

Copying Components to a BOM   A copy function can be used to add components to master BOMs and to the order-dependent BOM for a production order. For a master BOM, components can be copied from another master BOM as of a specified date. Alternatively, the components can be copied from the order-dependent BOM associated with a specified production order. You determine whether the components will add to or replace the existing components. Hence, the copy function can be used multiple times to generate incremental additions.

The copy function also works for an order-dependent BOM. The copy-to information identifies the specified production order number, and the copy-from can be another production order or a master BOM.

Mass Changes to Components based on Where-Used Information Where-used information provides the basis for a mass replace and a mass add function for maintaining components. You perform a mass change of BOM information using the periodic task *Change BOM Item*. You can select an item to be phased out or replaced, view the affected BOMs, selectively eliminate them from the update or change the required quantity, and then indicate when the new item should be phased in. This approach supports Option #1 for managing planned changes via date effectivities for a component.

Graphical Tools for Maintaining BOM Information   The BOM Designer provides a graphical tool for maintaining information about the BOM versions (and route versions) for an item. The form displays a multi-level product structure with an indented graphical format. You can edit or delete existing components, or add components via drag-and-drop from the displayed list of item master data. This graphical tool is employed in other contexts, such as displaying the BOM information during sales order entry.

Analyzing BOM Information   Analysis tools for BOM information include multi-level BOM reports, and a multi-level costed BOM with routing information (based on cost roll-up calculations). The analysis tools also include where-used inquiries about a component item and a master BOM.

There are two other types of where-used inquiries that reflect information about existing production orders and batch tracking. The first type includes single- and multi-level pegging to the sources of demand and supply. The second type includes forward and backward batch tracking throughout the product structure.

3.8 Using a Product Change Case to Maintain BOM Information

An alternative approach to maintaining BOM information involves the use of cases that specifically handle product changes. Cases are typically used to manage issues raised by customers, vendors or employees. However, you can assign a case category when creating a case so that it is designated as a product change case. The functionality for a product change case works differently than other types of cases. Each product change case represents an Engineering Change Order (ECO), and you define the items and BOM information affected by the ECO. The shortened term of an "ECO" will be used here as a synonym of the term "Product Change Case."

The key information for using a product change case consists of the associated items and BOM versions affected by the change. A simple-yet-typical scenario consists of an ECO to identify a planned change to an item's BOM version (and the relevant effectivity date). In this scenario, you can create a product change case for an item's existing BOM version. The product change case can then be used to define the new BOM version, and associated it and the new component items to the case. You can subsequently approve and activate the item's new BOM version. Another scenario consists of an ECO to identify a planned change to the BOM version for multiple items, such as replacing an existing component with a new component, and employing where-used information to identify the associated parent items and BOM versions impacted by the change. You can optionally enter detailed notes about the ECO and each associated item and/or BOM version, thereby providing a rationale and history of the changes.

The only required setup information consists of a user-defined case category that has been assigned a category type of Product Change. Most scenarios only need to define one case category, where a typical identifier is *Prod-Chg* or *ECO*. Some scenarios create more than one case category for product change cases, such as indicating different types of ECOs that have different validation criteria.

Each product change case is uniquely identified by a Case ID. After creating a case and a description, you can indicate progress (via the case status of opened, in-process, and closed or cancelled) and case resolution (of accept, reject or none). Some aspects of the functionality for a case do not necessarily apply to its use for ECO purposes. Examples include a case process (which consists of user-definable steps to follow when working on a case), a service level agreement (which defines a guaranteed response time), and knowledge articles.

A product change case can only manage planned changes to the BOM version for a manufactured item; it cannot support planned changes to a component's effectivity dates. While it can be used to support planned changes to the Route version for a manufactured item, this approach is not commonly employed for maintaining routing data.

3.9 Additional Case Studies

Case 3.1 Make-to-Order Production Strategy A basic variation in manufacturing involves the choice of production strategies as part of the S&OP game plans for an item. The two classic production strategies are termed make-to-stock (MTS) and make-to-order (MTO). In many cases, a make-to-order strategy does not require a link between the production order and the sales order for the item. In other cases, a make-to-order strategy requires this linkage. You can establish linked orders by first creating a production order from a sales order line for the end-item, and then scheduling this production order to automatically create the linked production orders for components (termed reference orders).

The reference orders reflect BOM information about components, where a BOM line type of *pegged supply* indicates a make-to-order component and a BOM line type of *vendor* indicates a buy-to-order component. Figure 3.4 illustrates how to create linkage between a sales order line item and a production order, and the impact of the BOM line type on creating linked production orders and linked purchase orders for components.

Figure 3.4 Make-to-Order Product with Linked Orders

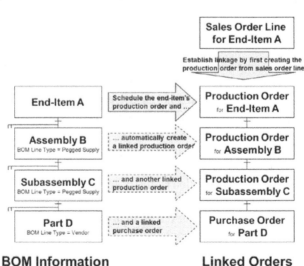

Case 3.2: Revision Levels for a Manufactured Item   A manufacturer employed the BOM versions to represent the revision levels for a manufactured item, such as revision A, B and C. The inventory resulting from production of different revision levels was treated as interchangeable by master scheduling logic. For reference purposes, the identifier assigned to each Master BOM represented a combination of the item number and revision level. The item's BOM version policies identified the effectivity dates for phasing out (and phasing in) these BOM versions. A complete change in a product was identified by a different item number, since it represented the maxim about changing form/fit/function.

Case 3.3: Kit Items   A manufacturing company sold kits of material, where a separate item (and associated master BOM) defined each kit's components. Several types of kits could be sold. One type of kit was priced and sold as a single item, and posting the sales invoice resulted in backflushing of the item's components. Another type of kit was priced and sold as separate component items. Each sales order line for a kit item was exploded into its components, thereby creating multiple line items with separate prices that were shipped and invoiced separately. Other scenarios involved the selection of kit components from a predefined list, pricing based on the sum of sales prices for kit components, returns of an entire kit or selected components, and selective printing of kit information on sales-related documents.[3]

Case 3.4: Phantoms for Intermediate BOM Levels   A toy company produced and sold cases of toys to retailers, where each case included boxes of the individual toy. Each box represented the consumer unit and an intermediate level of packaging. Each case and box of the toy had separate item numbers, with different UPC codes, weights and measurements. The box with an individual toy was treated as a phantom in the product structure because the packaging line could insert the toy into a box and pack them immediately into cases. It was sometimes stocked or sold separately.

Case 3.5: Engineering versus Production BOMs   The engineering department wanted to define a separate engineering BOM and then convert it into a BOM for production purposes. They defined a separate BOM version for a manufactured item that represented the engineering BOM. At the appropriate time, it was copied into a different BOM version for production purposes, and it was subsequently approved and activated for production. The starting effectivity date for the BOM version considered current inventories and other factors.

---

[3] See www.AXtension.com for additional information about their kitting add-on module for Dynamics AX.

Case 3.6: Cut-To-Size Materials   A fabricated products company needed to express BOM requirements in terms of the number of pieces of cut-to-size materials, such as steel rod and sheet metal, but did not want to create item numbers for each unique size. They solved the problem using the calculation formula and measurements for a component's required quantity. One example involved sheet metal purchased in pounds, costed and stocked in 5x10 sheets, and with component requirements expressed in square feet. Each parent item produced from the sheet metal required different height and width measurements, but only one master BOM to calculate the required square footage in sheet-size increments (50 square feet). This approach also identified purchasing and stockroom picking requirements for the raw materials, and provided cut-to-size instructions for production.

3.10 Executive Summary

Discrete manufacturers typically employ bills of material to model their product structure. This chapter summarized a typical business process for defining an item's bill of material, and described the key information about BOM version policies and BOM lines. It explained the different approaches to maintaining and analyzing BOM information, including the use of product change cases. Several case studies illustrated the use of BOM information, such as linked orders, kit items and cut-to-size material.

Chapter 4

Resources and Routings

Routing information provides a model of the processing steps for a manufactured item, expressed as operations that identify the production resource requirements. The routing information also provides the basis for calculating value-added costs, capacity planning and production scheduling of resources, reporting of actual labor and resource usage, and tracking progress through the processing steps. In addition, the bill of material often reflects considerations about an item's routing information, such as the material requirements for specific operations.

A single version of an item's routing may be sufficient in some scenarios, but many scenarios require multiple route versions in order to model variations in the manufacturing process for an item. For example, the route versions may reflect planned changes to the manufacturing process (such as new equipment or a different factory layout) or variations between sites producing the same item.

This chapter starts with the typical business processes to define production resources and routing information. Subsequent sections cover the definition of internal operations and maintenance of routing information. These considerations are reflected in the following sections within the chapter.

1. Typical Process to Define a Production Resource
2. Production Resources and Resource Groups
3. Define Capabilities and Assign to Resources
4. Define Competencies and Assign to Employees
5. Master Routings and Route Versions
6. Typical Process to Define an Item's Routing Information
7. Define Master Operations
8. Define an Internal Operation in a Routing
9. Scheduling Method: Job versus Operation Scheduling
10. Order-Dependent Routing for a Production Order
11. Maintain Routing information

4.1 Typical Process to Define a Production Resource

The typical process consists of several steps to define each production resource and its resource group. An internal resource often represents a machine, a specific employee, or a type of production worker. It can also represent some other capacity constraint or costing consideration. A resource group represents similar resources in close proximity within the same AX site. A resource or a resource group can then be specified as the resource requirement for a routing operation.

Additional steps may be involved for modeling resource capabilities or employee competencies. Resource capabilities, for example, can be used to model alternate resource logic based on a prioritized list of preferred resources or a minimum level of capability. Employee competencies apply to scenarios with highly skilled employees as a scheduling constraint, where you define an employee competency (such as skills, certifications or courses) as the resource requirement for an operation, and maintain information about each employee's competencies. Figure 4.1 illustrates these steps for three variations of production resources -- representing a machine, a type of production worker or a specific employee -- as illustrated by the three boxes within the figure. The process engineer role typically defines production resources and resource groups.

Figure 4.1 Typical Process to Define a Production Resource

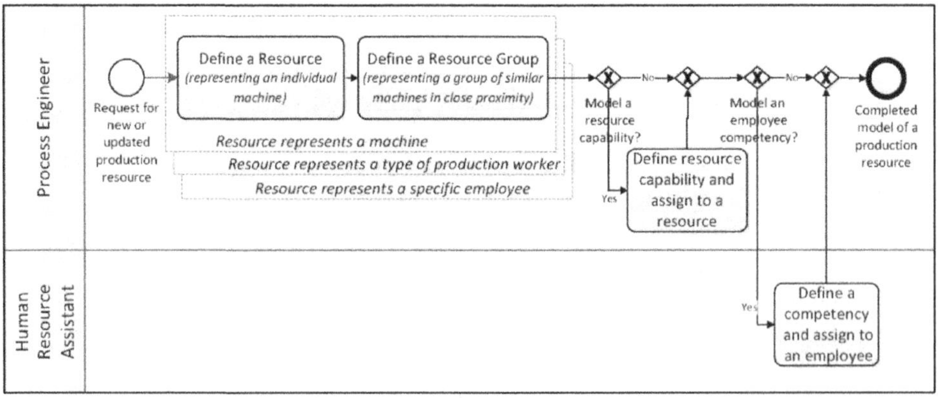

Define a Resource Representing a Machine The process engineer defines a production resource that represents a machine, and assigns it to a resource group that represents similar machines in close proximity within the same AX site.[1] A machine may subsequently be moved to a different site, which can be modeled in terms of validity dates for the assignment of the resource to a resource group. The basic information for a resource includes a calendar of working hours and a designation whether its available capacity should be considered finite or infinite. Since multiple time elements can be specified for performing an operation at the resource -- such as run time, transit time and queue times -- you may also need to designate the scheduling significance of each time element. The relevant costs (aka machine rate code) may also be assigned to the resource, such as the hourly costs for run time and setup time.

Define a Resource Representing a Specific Employee The process engineer defines a human resource to represent an individual employee, and assigns the employee number to the resource. The resource is also assigned to a resource group that represents similar workers in close proximity within the same AX site. An employee may subsequently be assigned to a different resource group, as identified by the validity dates of the assignment. The crew size requirements for an operation can be modeled by specifying the required resource group and the number of required resources.

Define a Resource Representing a Type of Production Worker The process engineer defines a human resource to represent a type of production worker, but does not assign an employee number to the human resource. Example identifiers for these resources could be Prod-Worker-1, Prod-Worker-2, and so forth. As noted above for modeling specific employees, you assign each resource to a resource group that represents similar workers in close proximity, and you can model an operation's crew size requirements by specifying the required resource group and the number of required resources.

Define a Resource Capability and Assign to a Resource The process engineer defines resource capabilities and assigns them to resources. A capability can be assigned to one or more resources, and a resource can have more than one capability assigned to it. The process engineer can then define a capability as the resource requirement of a routing operation. When assigning a capability to multiple resources, the process engineer can specify the priority associated with each resource so that the priorities will be considered by the scheduling logic. In addition, the process engineer can define a capability level for a resource, expressed as a numeric value (such as 50 tons for a press). The process engineer can then define the minimum required capability level as the

---

[1] A scenario involving a unique machine typically requires a resource group with only one resource that reflects the unique machine.

resource requirement for an operation so that the capability levels will be considered by scheduling logic in determining which resource should perform the operation.

Define a Competency and Assign to an Employee A human resource assistant typically defines employee-related competencies such as certifications, skills, and courses, and maintains the assignment of competencies to employees. As an illustrative example concerning certifications, you can define the possible types of certifications and assign a certification (and a starting date for the certification) to employees. The process engineer can then specify a required certification as part of the resource requirements for a routing operation. Similar steps apply to the use of skills and courses as the basis for human resource requirements.

4.2 Production Resources and Resource Groups

Resources and resource groups represent two of the primary approaches for specifying the resource requirements for a routing operation. The other primary approaches include resource capabilities and employee competencies, as explained in subsequent sections. A resource may represent a machine, an individual employee, a type of production worker, a tool, or some other type of capacity constraint or manufacturing cost. It may also represent a tightly linked group of machines or a manufacturing cell that can be treated as single resource. Each resource must belong to a resource group.[2] A resource group typically represents similar resources located in close proximity within the same site. You can specify a resource or a resource group as the resource requirement for a routing operation.

Identification of Resources and Resource Groups A resource has a unique identifier and description, and a resource group also has a unique identifier and description. Each resource must be assigned to a resource group, and changes in this assignment can be indicated by validity dates.

Type of Resource The common types consist of a machine or human resource, and sometimes a vendor when the scenario involves subcontracted production. Some suggested guidelines for identifying resources and resource groups are provided below.

---

[2] The Resource Lifecycle Management workspace identifies the resources not yet assigned to a resource group, and supports the assignment to a resource group. The workspace also provides links to related information such as calendars, resource capabilities, and the mass maintenance of resource requirements.

◆ *Machine.* A machine resource often represents a single machine, but it may also represent a tightly linked group of machines that acts as a single entity for capacity planning and scheduling purposes. The resource capacity for a single machine is typically expressed as one.

When defining a resource group related to machines (and then assigning machines to the group), the grouping typically represents machines in close physical proximity with similar characteristics in terms of capabilities and operating costs.

A machine resource is sometimes used to model a miscellaneous area comprised of a mixture of personnel and equipment performing various operations. This provides the basis for defining routing operations, and an approximation of costing, capacity planning, and scheduling considerations. The resource capacity provides an approximation of how many operations can be concurrently processed within the miscellaneous area.

◆ *Human Resource.* A human resource can represent a specific employee (by assigning the employee number) or a type of production worker (by not assigning an employee number). When defining a resource group related to human resources, the grouping typically represents a labor pool or a team of people in close physical proximity with similar characteristics in terms of capabilities and labor rates. In this way, you can model crew size requirements in a routing operation by specifying the resource group and the number of required resources within the group.

◆ *Vendor.* A vendor resource typically represents a specific subcontractor (with optional assignment of the vendor number) that performs subcontracted production using supplied material. A subsequent chapter provides further explanation of how to model subcontracted production (Chapter 15).

◆ *Tool.* A tool resource is rarely specified unless it represents a critical scheduling constraint. Examples of a tool include a serialized die, mold or re-useable fixture. A tool is typically specified as a secondary resource for performing an operation. A resource group for tooling generally represents several serial numbers of the exact same tool. A tool resource does not support tool inventory management or the tracking of tool cycle usage (e.g., for triggering replacement or rebuild). A serialized tool must be identified as an item to support these purposes.

◆ *Location.* A location resource is conceptually similar to a tool resource, and is rarely specified unless it represents a critical scheduling constraint. One example would a clean room. The clean room would typically be specified as a secondary resource for performing an operation. A resource group could represent several clean rooms. Modeling a location as a resource simply provides a scheduling constraint. Actual inventory locations must be defined in terms of the site, warehouse and bin location.

Guidelines for Specifying a Resource or Resource Group in a Routing Operation Several factors should be considered in choosing whether to designate a resource or a resource group for performing an operation. The following guidelines focus on machines and human resources.

◆ *Specify a Resource for the Operation.* This approach assumes the operation can only be performed at the specified machine, where the operation identifies the machine-specific times and costs. A similar assumption applies to a specified human resource, where the resource represents a specific employee.

◆ *Specify a Resource Group for the Operation* With machines, this approach assumes the operation can be performed on any machine within the group, and the machines have similar run times and cost structures. As part of defining a routing operation, you can optionally specify which machine will provide the default values for cost information and time requirements. The job scheduling logic will assign a specific machine (within the group) to an operation in order to meet the due date.

With human resources, the resource group typically represents a group of employees or production workers with interchangeable skills and similar hourly rates. When defining an operation for the resource group, you can specify the required number of people (aka crew size) for the operation. You can optionally specify which human resource will provide the default values for cost information. The job scheduling logic will assign specific human resources (within the group) to an operation in order to meet the due date and crew size requirements.

Changing the Assignment of a Resource to a Resource Group In a static environment, you assign a resource to a single resource group. In a dynamic environment with changing assignments, you indicate the expiration date for the current assignment, and also indicate the new assignment. For example, a piece of equipment or a person may be moved to a different site, which would be modeled by assigning the resource to a different resource group. Note that a site is assigned to a resource group, and the site applies to all resources assigned to the group.

Production Unit for a Resource Group   A user-defined production unit provides one approach for identifying an input warehouse and output warehouse related to production orders at the resources within a resource group. You assign a production unit to a resource group. The use of a production unit to define a component's warehouse source was described in a previous chapter (Section 3.5).

Production Input and Output Locations for a Resource Group   The assignment of a production input location to a resource group (or to individual resources within the group) is typically used to support the Advanced WMS approach to production order picking, where a picking work order delivers components to the relevant production input location. The use of a production input location to define a component's warehouse source was described in a previous chapter (Section 3.5).   In addition, the assignment of a production output location to a resource group indicates where to place the finished quantities of a production order.

Available Capacity for a Resource   A resource's available capacity is defined by two basic factors: the calendar defining the hours of operation and the capacity per hour.

◆ *Hours of Operation.* The calendar assigned to a resource defines the hours of operation (such as 7:00 a.m. to 4:00 p.m.) for each calendar day.   The calendar assigned to a human resource typically reflects the relevant shift. Exceptions to this calendar of daily working hours can be specified, such as specifying downtime or overtime.

◆ *Capacity per Hour.* A single resource that can perform one task at a time has a capacity of 1.00 during working hours.   However, a resource sometimes represents a number of people or machines, where more than one task can be performed at the same time.   The average number of concurrent tasks is termed the *resource capacity.*   With a capacity of 5, for example, up to 5 different operations can be scheduled concurrently for each hour of operation.

A third factor -- termed the *operations scheduling percentage* for a resource -- affects how scheduling logic views the resource's available capacity.   A scheduling percentage of 80%, for example, means that master scheduling logic will only consider 80% of the available capacity when assigning loads to the resource.   This approach provides flexibility for handling unexpected time requirements.

Infinite Versus Finite Available Capacity for a Resource A resource's available capacity can be designated as finite or infinite for scheduling purposes. An infinite capacity viewpoint means that scheduling logic ignores existing loads when scheduling a given order, but still considers constraints related to hours of operation and concurrent task capabilities to calculate operation durations. An analysis of resource load versus capacity can be used to identify overloaded periods, so that adjustments can be made to loads or available capacity.

A finite capacity viewpoint means that scheduling logic considers current loads (and the concurrent task capability) for each resource when scheduling a given order. Finite capacity considerations can be optionally included/excluded when performing the master scheduling task or when scheduling individual orders.

Designating Bottleneck Resources for Finite Capacity Planning Purposes The optional designation of a bottleneck resource can improve performance of master scheduling calculations. Additional master plan policies must be defined for the use of bottleneck scheduling and for three time fence policies related to bottleneck scheduling (the finite capacity time fence, the backward capacity time fence, and the bottleneck capacity time fence).

Efficiency The time requirements expressed in routing operations can be factored up or down based on the efficiency percentage assigned to the resource. The resource's efficiency percentage acts as a default in the resource's assigned calendar. The efficiency for selected working times (such as a lower efficiency for late night hours) can then be manually overridden in the calendar.

Resource Costs The costs associated with a resource are typically expressed in terms of hourly rates for setup and processing time. That is, you define hourly rates for a cost category, and assign the cost category to a resource. Different cost categories must be defined for each labor rate or machine rate, and different categories may be needed to differentiate the rates related to setup or run time. You also assign a cost group to a cost category, which supports cost group segmentation in the calculated costs for a manufactured item. The costs associated with setup and run times are normally included in the cost calculations. You can selectively exclude these costs based on the policies embedded in the Routing Group assigned to a resource. A subsequent chapter provides further explanation of product costing, and the definition of costs for resources (Section 5.5).

Time Reporting and Auto-Deduction Policies The time associated with processing and setup can be manually reported or auto-deducted, as indicated by *Automatic Route Consumption* policies embedded in the Routing Group assigned to a resource.

Summarized Information for a Resource You can view summarized information about a resource's available capacity, actual reported time, and the capacity utilization percentage for the current accounting period, current year to date, and the preceding year. A resource's load inquiry summarizes available capacity, expected load, and a capacity utilization percentage for various time increments, such as months and weeks. It also provides drill down to the orders causing the expected load.

Aggregate Capacity and Loads for a Resource Group The aggregate capacity for a resource group is based on the sum of available capacity for the related resources. The aggregate load for the resource group includes the time requirements for its related resources.   An analysis of aggregate load versus capacity can help anticipate overloaded periods.

4.3 Define Capabilities and Assign to Resources

Capabilities provide one approach for modeling the resource requirements of a routing operation, and they apply to any type of resource. They build on the use of resources described in the previous section. You assign a capability to one or more resources, and a resource can have more than one capability assigned to it. In addition, you specify the required capability for a performing a routing operation.

Each capability has a user-defined identifier and description, and you specify a list of which resources can provide the capability. Conversely, you can assign a capability to resource. The following subsections provide guidelines concerning the definition and use of resource capabilities.

Specify Date Effectivities of the Resource Capability Each resource assigned to a capability can be assigned a starting and ending effectivity date. A resource can be listed more than once with different effectivity dates, typically to represent a capability that cannot be performed for a period of time. When a requirement date for the capability falls outside of the effective period, the resource will not be scheduled.

Assign Priorities to Support Alternate Resource Logic Each resource assigned to a capability can be assigned a numeric priority, where a value of 0 (or 1) represents the highest priority. The priority provides the basis for alternate resource logic in scheduling calculations.[3] That is, the resource with the highest

---

[3] A policy - termed *primary resource selection* - determines whether scheduling logic assigns resources based on *duration* or *priority*. Selecting a policy value of *priority* supports alternate resource logic based on priorities.

priority will be considered first by the scheduling logic. The resource with the next-highest priority will only be considered when the requirement date cannot be met.

Specify the Level of Capability to Support Alternate Resource Logic
The level of capability provides an additional basis for determining whether a resource can satisfy the capability. You specify the capability level as numeric value. In a similar fashion, you specify a value for the minimum level needed as part of the resource requirements in a routing operation. The scheduling logic will only consider resources in the list with an equal or higher value than the minimum level needed.

An example concerning presses illustrates how to use these two values. Let's say we have three machine resources that represent a 20-ton press, a 50-ton press, and a 100-ton press. The first step is to define a capability termed Press, and assign the three resources to the capability. The three resources are assigned a capability level of 20, 50 and 100 respectively. As the second step, you assign the minimum level needed to perform a routing operation requiring the Press capability. Let's say the value of the minimum level needed is 40. At this point, the scheduling logic considers the requirement specified for the operation (of 40) in selecting which resource can satisfy the requirement, which means only the 50-ton and 100-ton presses would be considered.

Specify the Capability as the Resource Requirement for a Routing Operation One or more capabilities can be specified as the resource requirements for a routing operation. Since the required capability may be satisfied by different resources, you should specify the approximate costs for performing the operation. These hourly rates can be manually specified using the cost category fields, or the cost categories can be initially populated by specifying a "costing resource" for the operation.

Case 4.1: Preferred Equipment for a Capability The production supervisor wanted to schedule production using the optimal packaging line (out of the three possible packaging lines). When the optimal packaging line was fully booked, the production could be scheduled on another line. To support this logic, the operation's resource requirements (in the route version for each manufactured item) were defined for a "packaging line" capability, and the capability was assigned to the three packaging lines along with a priority

The policy can be company-wide or site-specific, as defined on the Scheduling Parameters or Scheduling Parameters by Site form within the Master Planning setup information.

sequence. In this way, the scheduling logic assigns the optimal line to meet the production due date. If the due date cannot be met, the scheduling logic assigns a different line based on the prioritized list.

Case 4.2: Preferred Equipment based on Minimum Capability The production supervisor wanted to schedule production using the optimal packaging line (out of the three possible packaging lines). One packaging line could only handle small packages, another line could handle small or medium packages (but not large packages), and the third line could handle any package size. To support this logic, the operation's resource requirements (in the route version for each manufactured item) were defined for a "packaging line" capability and a minimum capability level of 1, 2 or 3 (that represented the three package sizes). The capability and a capability level were also assigned to the three packaging lines. In this way, the scheduling logic would only assign production to a packaging line that could meet the minimum required capability. For example, large packages were only assigned to the packaging line that could handle them.

4.4 Define Competencies and Assign to Employees

Some production environments require scheduling of highly-skilled employees with specific competencies, such as a certification, course or skill level. After defining a competency, you maintain the related information about each employee's competencies as part of the employee master information. You also define the competency as one of the resource requirements for a routing operation. This approach to resource requirements only applies to human resources representing individual employees where the employee number has been specified. The following subsections provide guidelines concerning the definition and use of employee competencies.

Employee Skills A skill has a user-defined identifier and description, and also a rating model consisting of a rating and skill level. You assign an actual skill (and a starting date for the skill) to an employee, and an employee can have more than one skill. In addition, you can specify the skill as a resource requirement for performing a routing operation.

Employee Certifications A certification type has a user-defined identifier and description. You assign a certification type (and a starting date for the certification) to an employee, and an employee can have more than one certification. In addition, you can specify the certificate as a resource requirement for performing a routing operation.

Employee Course   A course has a user-defined identifier and description. You assign a course (and a completion date for the course) to an employee, and an employee can have more than one course.   In addition, you can specify the course as a resource requirement for performing a routing operation.

Employee Self-Service Workspace for Updating an Employee Competency   This workspace enables an employee to add information about a skill (and skill level) or a certificate type (and the start and end dates), and to view their registered courses.

4.5 Master Routings and Route Versions

The concept of a master routing enables you to define it once, and then assign it to multiple items with the same production process.   When you create a master routing, the identifier (termed a *Route Number*) can be automatically or manually assigned, as defined by the number sequence policy for Route Numbers.   Manual assignment should be used when the master routing identifier needs to be meaningful, such as the process specification for a common routing or the item number for an item-specific routing.

After creating a master routing identifier, you can define the associated operations and also assign the master routing to relevant items.   Each assignment is termed a *Route Version*, and a manufactured item can have multiple route versions.   Each route version must be site-specific, and the associated operations must reflect resources within the site.   Master scheduling logic will use an item's site-specific routing version based on the site of the requirement.

Create and Assign a Master Routing   There are two basic approaches to create and assign master routings, as described below.   Each assignment is termed a *Route Version.*

◆   *Create a new routing for an item.*   This approach starts from a selected item (on the Released Products form), where you access its routing information in order to create a new master routing and define its operations.   The new master routing is automatically assigned to the item.   There is a single approval step, which results in approval of the master routing and the route version.

As an alternative to creating a new master routing for an item, you can assign an existing one to the item. This alternative represents a "new" assignment for an existing master routing; the assignment can also be "deleted". Each assignment requires a separate approval step. The assignment of a master routing to relevant items is also employed in the second approach.

◆ *Create a master routing and assign to items.* This approach starts from the list of master routings (termed the All Routes form), where you create a master routing and its operations, and then assign it to the relevant items.[2] There is an approval step for the master routing, and a separate approval step for each assignment (aka the route version). The creation of a master routing can also originate from the first approach, so that it can be subsequently assigned to other items.

Approved and Active Route Versions   A master routing and a route version must be approved, as described above. You can optionally employ electronic signatures as part of the approval process, as previously described for approving BOM information.

Only an approved route version for a manufactured item can be marked as active. The active route version for a manufactured item will normally be used in planning and cost calculations. There are several scenarios requiring multiple active route versions for an item, and even multiple approved-but-not active route versions, as described in the next topic.

Rationale for Multiple Route Versions for a Manufactured Item   A manufactured item can have multiple active route versions that reflect different sites, non-overlapping validity periods, and/or different quantity breakpoints. Other route versions may be approved but not active, typically to model an alternate production process.   The reasons for multiple route versions are explained below.

◆ *Routing Variations between Sites Producing the Same Manufactured Item.* The site-specific route versions reflect variations in the resources and operations for producing the item.

◆ *Planned Changes with Effectivity Dates.* The multiple route versions can represent planned changes to the production process, where each route version has a different validity period. For example, a manufactured item

---

[2] The assignment of master routings to a manufactured item can be assisted by an attribute (the Item Group) assigned to each master routing. Based on this attribute, the drop-down list of master routings can display the subset with an Item Group that matches the manufactured item.

may have two route versions to indicate planned changes, where one route version is valid until date X and the other route version is valid starting on date X+1.

◆ *Variations due to Order Quantities.* The multiple route versions can represent variations in the preferred production process for larger order quantities, where each route version has a different quantity breakpoint. For example, a route version can reflect use of a faster equipment for producing a large order quantity.

◆ *Alternate Routings.* Additional route versions can represent alternate processes for producing the manufactured item. The alternate would be an approved-but-not-active route version that could be specified for a manually-created production order or rework order. It could also be specified for a sales order line item (for a make-to-order product) or for a BOM line about a manufactured component (for a make-to-order component), so that scheduling logic employs the specified route version rather than the active route version.

◆ *Routings for Prototypes or Production Ramp-up.* A different route version may identify the production process for prototypes or different stages of production ramp-up.

In summary, a manufactured item can have multiple active route versions that reflect different sites, non-overlapping validity periods, and/or different quantity breakpoints. An item can also have approved-but-not-active route versions.

Case 4.3 Preferred Equipment based on Production Quantity The production supervisor at a manufacturing firm wanted to schedule production using the optimal equipment for small and large order quantities. The large order quantities (over 1,000) were produced on larger faster equipment. To support this logic, two different route versions were defined for the relevant manufactured items, where the quantity breakpoint for one route version reflected 1,000 units. This route version contained an operation with resource requirements for handling a large quantity, and the other route version contained an operation with resource requirements for handling the small quantity. In this way, master scheduling logic will assign the optimal route version to a planned production order based on the required quantity.

4.6 Typical Process to Define an Item's Routing

A typical business process to define routing information builds on an understanding of master routings and route versions. In summary, you define a master routing consisting of one or more operations and assign it to the applicable manufactured items. Each assignment is termed a route version, and the item's route version policies specify the relevant site and validity dates. In many cases, an item may require multiple route versions to reflect planned changes in the production process or variations between sites producing the same item. As part of defining an operation in a master routing, you identify an operation number, the resource requirement, and a master operation identifier. You define these master operations beforehand, so that an operation automatically inherits the resource requirements from the master operation. You can optionally review the feasibility of the resource requirements after completing the assignment of a master routing to an item. You can then approve and activate the item's route version, or simply approve it. These steps and their applicable roles are illustrated in Figure 4.2 and described below.

Figure 4.2 Typical Process to Define an Item's Routing

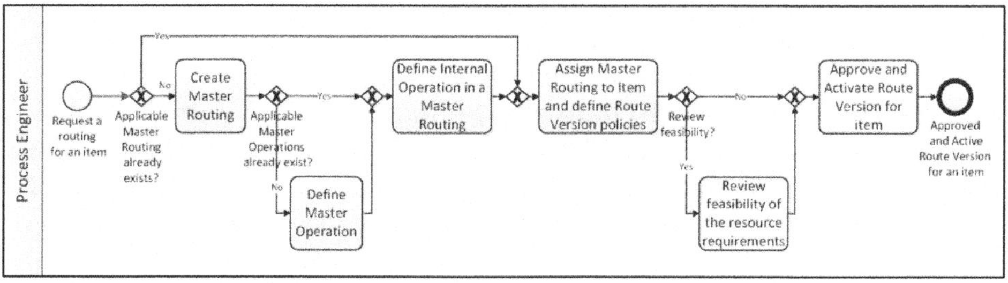

Create Master Routing   The process engineer typically creates a Master Routing and its operations so that it can be assigned to items going through the same production process. As an alternative starting point, the process engineer can start from an item and create a Master Routing, which is automatically assigned to the item.

Define a Master Operation   The process engineer employs the Master Operation concept to help minimize data maintenance efforts. By defining the resource requirements and applicability rules of a Master Operation, the process engineer can simply specify the Master Operation identifier in a routing operation, and the operation inherits the resource requirements. A Master Operation may have more than one applicability rule (and its associated resource requirements), such as a different applicability rule for a different group of items.

Changing the resource requirements for the Master Operation will automatically update all applicable operations.

Some scenarios do not employ the Master Operation concept. In these scenarios, the process engineer simply defines a Master Operation identifier without the applicability rule and associated resource requirement. An identifier must still be specified for a routing operation, where the process engineer must define the resource requirements for the operation (since nothing is inherited). However, the system will automatically track use of the Master Operation identifier by creating an applicability rule, such as the specific item number and master routing. In this way, the process engineer can still maintain the resource requirements using the Master Operation form.

Define an Internal Operation in a Master Routing For each operation, the process engineer assigns an operation number, a master operation identifier, the resource requirement, and the time requirements. The operation number can also be specified for relevant BOM components to provide linkage to the routing operation.

Some scenarios have an operation with one or more secondary resources. For example, the secondary resources of a machine operator and a tool may apply to the primary resource of a machine.

Assign Master Routing to item and define the Route Version policies The process engineer defines an item's route version policies, which include the Master Routing identifier, the relevant site, the validity dates, and an optional quantity breakpoint for a quantity-sensitive route version.

Review feasibility of the resource requirements for an Item's Route Version The process engineer analyzes route feasibility to determine whether applicable resources exist to satisfy the resource requirements of operations in an item's route version. For example, an operation's resource requirements may be infeasible due to lack of an assigned resource group (for a resource), or the lack of capabilities or employee competencies with valid dates. Attempts to activate an infeasible route version result in a soft warning message, and an option to review route feasibility. As a supplemental approach, the process engineer can also analyze availability of applicable resources when defining a master operation or specific operation within a routing.

Approve and Activate Route Version for Item The process engineer approves and activates an item's route version to enable actual usage on production orders and in planning/costing calculations. Attempts to activate an infeasible route version result in a soft warning message, and an option to review route feasibility. The process engineer may approve and activate multiple route versions for an item to reflect different sites, validity periods, or quantity breakpoints. In addition, the process designer may simply approve an item's route version but not activate it.

4.7 Define Master Operations

The concept of a master operation is central to the definition of routing operations within AX. A master operation (termed *Operation*) has a unique user-defined identifier and a description, and you define master operations on the Operations form. The identifier typically has some meaning so that its significance is easily understood, such as an abbreviation for an operation or a process specification number. An identifier for a master operation must be specified for each routing operation. The master operation provides default values for the operation's information such as the required resource and associated time. Changing the values for a master operation will automatically update the information on the associated routing operations, subject to applicability rules.

The applicability rules for a master operation represent a key related concept. In defining a master operation, you can specify one or more sets of data that will serve as default values in a given routing operation. Each set has an applicability rule. For example, a set of data could apply to a specified group of items, and an additional set of data could apply to another group of items. The combination of an applicability rule and a set of data is termed an *Operation Relation*.

The applicability rule can reflect a specific item, a group of items (based on the Item Group) or all items. In addition, the applicability rule can reflect a specific master routing or all master routings. These applicability rules reflect decreasing levels of specificity. When multiple applicability rules have been defined, the most specific level will be used to inherit values from a master operation.

The applicability rule and set of data (aka the Operation Relation) can be specified when you initially define a master operation. The set of data provides default values when the master operation is specified for a routing operation.

Manually overriding the values on a routing operation will automatically create an additional applicability rule for the master operation, and the set of data reflects the manually-overridden values. The new applicability rule indicates the item and master routing in which you performed the manual override. In this way, subsequent changes to the master operation will only affect the one routing operation.

The use of master operations varies from company to company. Many companies already employ the concept of master operations, and they can replicate their current conceptual model within AX. If the concept of master operations does not apply, you can simply create a master operation without any applicability rules or data. When you specify the master operation in a routing operation, no values will be inherited and you must define them. This will automatically create an Operation Relation for the master operation.

4.8 Define an Internal Operation in a Routing

The critical information for an internal operation consists of an operation number, a master operation identifier, the resource requirement, and the time requirements. Previous sections described the various methods for defining a resource requirement and the concept of a master operation. This section explains the other aspects of defining an internal operation. A subsequent chapter explains the definition of an external operation for subcontracted production (Section 15.5).

Operation Number The operation number provides a unique numeric identifier for each operation within a routing, and the basis for scheduling a serial routing. The system automatically assigns new operation numbers in increments of 10 but this operation number can be overridden. The use of operation numbers has several implications as described below.

♦ *Sequence the operations in a multistep routing.* The operation number itself does not provide sequencing logic. For sequencing purposes, each operation requires additional information about the next operation number, whether you are modeling a serial or parallel sequence.

♦ *Identify the last operation within a routing.* You must identify which operation represents the last operation in a routing (with a value of zero "0" in the Next Operation field). This information is helpful when reporting actual production activity for the last operation, so that reporting the units completed at the last operation can automatically update the finished quantity for the production order.

♦ *Identify the material components required for an operation.* Assigning the operation number to the required material (in the BOM line information) allows master scheduling logic to synchronize material due dates with the operation start date. It provides the basis for calculating the impact of operation scrap percentages on the associated material requirements. It also provides the basis for populating the picking list for a production order based on the started quantity for the operation number.

◆ *Provide an identifier to report actual production activity.* You report actual time and/or unit completions against an order number and operation number.

◆ *Indicate when tests should be performed during production of an item.* The required tests for an item (via the automatic creation of a quality order) can reflect a specified operation number within the routing.

Primary Versus Secondary Resources (Operation Priority)   Each operation requires a primary resource, and most production environments can be modeled using operations with just a primary resource.   Some production environments have operations requiring one or more secondary resources, such as the people and tools for running a machine.   The operation's primary resource represents the pacing resource that determines operation duration.   The same operation number must be assigned to each secondary resource, and the same time requirements apply because it is not the pacing resource.   Operations with the same operation number are termed *simultaneous operations.*

The type of linkage between a primary and secondary resource affects scheduling logic, where the link type can be hard or soft.   That is, you can indicate that the secondary resources for an operation must start at the same time as the primary resource (a link type of hard).   The alternative allows a time gap (a link type of soft or blank).

Case 4.4   Simultaneous Requirements for a Machine, Operator and Tool   One production process at an equipment company required a dedicated machine, a skilled operator, and a specialized mold.   In order to model these simultaneous resource requirements for the operation, the route version for each manufactured item contained three lines with the same operation number.   The first line identified the primary resource requirement of the machine, since this acted as the pacing resource.   The next two lines identified the secondary resource requirements for the skilled operator and the mold tool.

Case 4.5   Use Secondary Resources for Costing Purposes   The routing information for several manufactured items consisted of a single operation that involved a single primary resource representing the equipment and multiple secondary resources representing the different types of labor to run the equipment.   The different types of labor were assigned different labor rates and cost groups, and the overheads varied for each type of labor.   The secondary resources were used for costing purposes rather than scheduling purposes.

Resource Requirement   Each operation must include at least one resource requirement.   The resource requirement can be expressed for a resource, a resource group, a resource capability or an employee competency, as previously described.

Resource Quantity The resource quantity indicates the number of resources required to perform the operation. It can be illustrated by a resource group for human resources containing resources that represent individual people. For example, a run time requirement of 3 hours and a resource quantity of 2 people would be interpreted as a total load of 6 hours (for the resource group). The detailed scheduling method creates a load of 3 hours for 2 different resources (people).

Time Requirements Time requirements are normally expressed as hours per unit or units per hour. They can also be expressed in minutes or days (which applies to all time elements for the operation), but cost and planning calculations will convert these time requirements back into hours.[3] This approach to defining time requirements is termed a "standard" resource consumption policy, and you assign the policy to an operation. The next subsection describes some alternate approaches to defining time requirements, whereas this section focuses on the standard approach.

The time requirements are typically defined for run time and optional setup time, but some scenarios employ additional time elements to model the production process. The following considerations apply to the definition of time requirements for various time elements.

◆ *Run Time per Unit* The run time is typically expressed per 1 unit. It can be expressed for a different quantity, such as the run time per 100 units (as defined by the process quantity field). Alternatively, you can define a run rate, such as specifying a time requirement of 1 hour and a process quantity that represents the run rate per hour.

◆ *Setup Time.* Setup time represents a fixed requirement before starting the run time for production. Short setup times are typically not defined.

◆ *Changeover Time.* Changeover time represents a fixed requirement after completing the run time for production. It is typically modeled by the "queue after" time element within AX, as described in the next point.

◆ *Other Time Elements for Scheduling and Capacity Planning Purposes.* Other time elements include the number of hours for queue time before and after the operation, and the transit time to the next operation. Many scenarios employ different names for these time elements, such as a changeover time or cooling time rather than a queue time after the operation. Several policies

---

[3] Time requirements expressed in hours reflects an "hours per time unit" value of 1. This "hours per time unit" field can also be used to define time requirements in minutes (a value of 1/60 or .0167) or days (a value of 24) or some other user-specified interval.

(embedded in the Route Group assigned to the operation) determine the impact of time requirements for these time elements, since they can optionally consume capacity.   The impact of route group policies are described in a following subsection.

◆   *Overlapping Operations.* An operation can have a specified overlap quantity (also termed the transfer batch quantity) so that the next operation can start before operation completion.

Alternative Approaches to Defining Time Requirements An alternative approach to defining time requirements may apply to a machine and its machine cycles. The capacity of the machine is expressed as the number of cycles per hour, and the resource requirement identifies the number of required cycles to produce an item. This approach to defining time requirements is termed a "capacity" resource consumption policy, and you assign the policy to an operation. A slight variation builds on the use of machine cycles, and typically applies to a machine using a mold or die to produce a "batch quantity" of an item. This approach to defining time requirements is termed a "resource batch" resource consumption policy, and you assign the policy to an operation.

Time Requirements and the Impact of Route Group Policies A route group defines a set of policies that determine how an operation's time requirements will be treated. With run time and setup time, for example, the associated costs normally included in cost calculations, and the associated times are normally included in scheduling and capacity planning. In many cases, multiple route groups are defined with different policies about the treatment of each time element, so that the route group can be assigned to relevant operations.

Yield Percentage for an Operation The planned yield percentage for an operation affects the required runtime and the materials tied to the operation. The system automatically calculates and displays an accumulated yield percentage for each operation in a routing with multiple operations.

Cost Data for an Operation The cost data for an operation includes the cost categories defining the hourly rates. The cost categories would normally default from the required resource, and can be overridden. You can optionally specify which resource should be used for costing purposes (aka the costing resource) in order to populate the cost categories; the costing resource has no other purpose. In addition, the costs associated with an operation can be optionally ignored in cost calculations, as determined by the policies embedded in the Route Group assigned to the operation.

Reporting Operation Time The auto-deduction policies for an operation reflect the Route Group assigned to the operation.

Operation Description The operation description consists of unlimited free-form text, and the optional use of documents such as a Word file or an image.

4.9 Scheduling Method: Job versus Operation Scheduling

The scheduling logic within AX is slightly different for the two scheduling methods, which are termed *operation scheduling* and *job scheduling*. The term *job scheduling* may be confusing to those people that think of a job as synonymous with a production order or project, but in this context job refers to the individual time elements within an operation. These time elements can include setup, process and queue times. The scheduling significance of these time elements is defined within the Route Group assigned to an operation.

The ability to handle detailed time elements represents a primary difference between the two scheduling methods. A second key difference concerns the detailed information about employee competencies. The job scheduling method can handle these details, whereas the operation scheduling method cannot. The differentiating factors between the scheduling methods are summarized in Figure 4.3 and explained below.

Figure 4.3 Comparison of Scheduling Methods

		Scheduling Method	
		Operations Scheduling	**Job Scheduling**
Differentiating Factors	Scheduling Focus	Resource Group	Resource
	Capacity Planning	Detailed (by Resource) and Aggregate (by Group)	Detailed (by Resource) and Aggregate (by Group)
	Scheduling Capabilities		Schedule detailed time elements (aka jobs) Lock a job and synchronize related time elements Assign a resource based on capabilities or employee competencies Support alternative approaches to the definition of time requirements (e.g. via machine cycles) Perform block scheduling via properties Use of Gantt Chart to display production schedule
	Time Granularity	Schedule by date	Schedule by date and time
	Printed Shop Traveler	Route Card	Job Card
	Reporting Operation Time and Unit Completions	Use Route Card Journal	Use Job Card Journal or Route Card Journal
	Computer Processing Time	Faster	Slower

◆ *Job Scheduling Method.* This method supports (1) scheduling the time elements for an operation, (2) assigning resources based on a requirement for capabilities or employee competencies, (3) block scheduling based on a property, and (4) use of a Gantt Chart to display production schedule information. Minor differences include the printed shop traveler, the approach for reporting operation time and unit completions, and computer processing time.

◆ *Operation Scheduling Method.* This method does not support some scheduling capabilities, as mentioned above.

With the master scheduling task, the scheduling logic based on routing data only applies within the time horizon defined by a capacity time fence (expressed in days). You define the capacity time fence as one of the policies within the coverage group assigned to an item, or as one of the policies for a master plan. In most cases, the capacity time fence reflects near-term scheduling requirements (such as a 30 day horizon), although a longer horizon (such as 365 days) would be used to calculate long-term capacity requirements.

4.10 Order-Dependent Routing for a Production Order

An order-dependent routing refers to the routing operations attached to a production order. It is also termed the Production Route. Changes to an order-dependent routing do not affect the master routing. Creation and maintenance of the order-dependent routing reflect several rules, which parallel the rules for maintaining an order-dependent BOM.

◆ Creation of a production order can also create an order-dependent routing.

◆ The order-dependent routing initially reflects the item's route version that was used to create the production order. In most cases, this will be inherited from the active route version for the site and start date on the production order. However, you can manually specify a different route version for the item when manually creating the production order, where the route version can be approved-but-not-active.

◆ The order-dependent routing contains the routing operations of a phantom.

◆ You can modify the operations in an order-dependent routing at any time prior to reporting the production order as ended.

◆ You can copy operations to an order-dependent routing -- such as copying from another production order or a Master Routing -- prior to reporting a production order as scheduled.

◆ Time can only be reported when the operation sequence number exists in the order-dependent routing.

4.11 Maintain Routing Information

Routing information can be maintained using several approaches. You typically maintain multiple master routings in order to support multiple active route versions for an item, and a copy function provides one approach to data maintenance. Other approaches include the master operation concept to support mass updates to routing operations, and a mass update wizard for updating the assignment of resource requirements within master operations. Another aspect of maintaining routing information includes the review of route feasibility, since a routing may be infeasible due to the lack of applicable resources for one or more operations. These approaches to routing maintenance are summarized below.

Maintain Multiple Active Route Versions for an Item   Planned changes can be identified by the validity dates assigned to the route versions for an item, so that multiple route versions can be approved and active. Multiple active route versions may also be necessary to support site-specific or quantity-sensitive versions.

Use the Copy Function to Populate Operations in a Master Routing
The copy function involves a destination for the "copy to" master routing, and a source for the "copy from" information. Initiating the copy function for a selected master routing will identify the copy to destination. The copy function is also provided when you create an additional route version for an item.

Mass Updates via the Master Operation Concept   In order to support mass updates, the applicability rule for a master operation must reflect a group of items (or all items). In this way, changes to the master operation will automatically update the operations that specified the master operation identifier. If an applicability rule only applies to a single item and its master routing, the changes to the master operation only updates the single occurrence. A previous section described the use of master operations (Section 4.7).

Mass Update the Assignment of Resource Requirements within Master Operations   A mass update wizard uses information about existing resource requirements within master operations so that you can delete the existing resource requirement, replace it with a different one, or add another resource requirement. The wizard -- termed the Maintain Resource Requirements wizard -- consists of several steps and their associated screens, as described below.

◆ *Step 1: Identify an existing resource requirement based on Search Criteria.*
Use the first screen (labeled Search Criteria) to specify the search criteria for
existing resource requirements, such as a specific resource or capability.
More than one search criteria can be specified. The search criteria can
optionally include the identifier of a master operation.

◆ *Step 2: Specify the mass update action.* Use the second screen (labeled
Action) to specify whether you want to delete, replace or add to the existing
resource requirement. As part of this step, you also indicate the option for
where to apply the action. The option would be "routing" information in this
scenario, but another option could be the order-dependent routing
information (aka production route).[4]

◆ *Step 3: Specify the new resource requirement.* The third screen (labeled New
Resource Requirements) is only displayed when the action involves adding
to or replacing an existing resource requirement.

◆ *Step 4: Review a summary of the proposed mass update.* The final screen
(labeled Summary) summarizes the information from the first three steps.
You can accept the proposed changes, go back to a previous step and make
adjustments, and cancel the proposed mass-update. Accepting the proposed
mass update will change the resource requirements within master operations.

Maintain Routing Information using a Product Change Case   An
alternative approach to maintain routing information involves the use of cases
that specifically handle product changes. Each product change case represents an
Engineering Change Order (ECO), and it typically applies to maintaining the
BOM versions of a manufactured item as described in the previous chapter
(Section 3.8).

**Review Feasibility of the Resource Requirements for Operations
within a Routing**   A key aspect of data maintenance involves reviewing the
feasibility of the resource requirements for an item's route version. A routing
may be infeasible due to the lack of applicable resources for one or more
operations.

Analysis Tools for Routing Information   Analysis tools for an item's
routing information include where-used inquiries about a resource, a master
routing and a master operation. They also include a multilevel cost analysis,
which shows the cost contributions of resources and related overheads in the
calculated cost of a manufactured item.

---

[4] The other options include project-related information about resource requirements (termed hour forecasts) and
custom product-related information about resource requirements defined in a Product Configuration Model or a
Product Model. Chapter 19 describes the configuration technologies for custom products.

4.12 Additional Case Studies

Case 4.6: Integration with an Equipment Maintenance Application

The plant manager at a discrete manufacturer wanted to implement an integrated equipment maintenance application, also termed an Enterprise Asset Management (EAM) application. A key issue concerned the coordination between production planning and maintenance scheduling. The plant manager preferred a software module built using the standard AX constructs rather than a separate best-of-breed software package with its own constructs and interface requirements. With standard AX constructs, for example, the spare parts for equipment maintenance could be defined in the item master, procured using requisitions and purchase orders, and tracked via inventory transactions in the same way as other purchased items. Three aspects of integration were especially important. First, the downtime at machines (reflecting planned and ad hoc maintenance) must be identified and coordinated in the production schedules. Second, the triggers for planned maintenance must reflect actual and projected equipment usage. And third, inventory tracking was required for the tools used in maintenance, so that each serialized tool could be easily checked out and checked in. Using these guidelines, they implemented an integrated EAM system to support their equipment maintenance requirements.[5]

Case 4.7: Feasibility of a Routing with New Equipment

A company was implementing a change in equipment that also required skilled operators with the relevant equipment certification. As part of the new route versions for manufactured items produced by the equipment, an operation specified the resource requirements for the new equipment (as a primary resource) and for the employee certification (as a secondary resource). One concern was the match-up between the equipment availability date (defined by the effectivity date for its resource group) and the availability of certified operators (defined by their certification date). This date could be analyzed by reviewing the feasibility of the resource requirements for an item's route version.

Case 4.8: Burn-In Period after Completing Production

The production process for a manufactured item involved a burn-in period after completing assembly at a final assembly work center. The number of burn-in hours was specified using the "queue after" time element. This approach requires the definition of a Route Group in which "queue after" time is designated as working time (but does not consume resource capacity), and the assignment of this Route Group to the operation performed by the final assembly work center.

---

[5] For more information about the integrated EAM system for AX (called DAXEAM), see www.UXCEclipse.com.

4.13 Executive Summary

A master routing represents a model of production activities for a manufactured item. Assignment of multiple master routings to an item (termed route versions) can support site-specific variations, planned changes, preferred equipment based on production quantity, and alternate equipment. Each operation within a route version defines the resource requirements and associated time requirements. The case studies illustrated variations in the use of routing data, such as designating the preferred equipment and integration with equipment maintenance.

Chapter 5

Product Costing

Product cost information defines the value of an item's inventory transactions. The primary variations in product costing involve standard versus actual costs, and purchased versus manufactured items. For a manufactured item, the calculation of product costs reflects the item's BOM and routing information. These calculations can be used to project future costs, simulate the impact of cost changes, analyze cost reduction opportunities, analyze profitability, and calculate an item's suggested sales price.

Product cost information represents one of the more complex and critical aspects of an integrated ERP system. As an explanatory approach, we'll start with the foundation of costing versions which contain cost records about items, labor rates and overheads. The foundation also requires an understanding of the terminology about item cost records and cost calculations, and the significance of cost groups. We'll build on this foundation in order to explain costs for purchased items and the cost calculations for manufactured items. These topics are reflected in the following sections within the chapter.

1. Summary of Costing Versions
2. Terminology for Item Cost Records and Cost Calculations
3. Significance of Cost Groups
4. Standard Costs for Purchased Items
5. Define Resource Costs via Cost Categories
6. Define Overhead Costs via Overhead Formulas
7. Standard Cost Calculations for Manufactured Items
8. Planned Cost Calculations for Manufactured Items
9. Variations of Cost Calculations
10. Summary of Standard Cost Variances
11. Actual Costing Approaches

5.1 Summary of Costing Versions

A costing version contains the cost records for items, labor rates and overhead formulas. You designate whether a costing version contains standard costs or planned costs. With a version containing standard costs, the cost records about items define their site-specific standard costs. A costing version containing planned costs is used for simulation purposes, such as calculating a manufactured item's planned cost.

Different Costing Versions for Standard Costs The significance of a costing version depends on how you conceptualize your approach for maintaining standard costs. A common approach consists of multiple costing versions that represent standard costs for different calendar years (or quarters). With this approach, you maintain all item cost records within one costing version that represents the current calendar year, and use an additional costing version for maintaining next year's standard costs. You can copy the active cost records from one costing version to create pending cost records in the other cost version, thereby providing a starting point for updating next year's standard costs. These pending cost records would then be activated at the beginning of the year.

Other approaches reflect a different conceptualization. For example, multiple costing versions can represent site-specific standard costs for different sites, or each costing version can represent incremental changes to standard costs (including the standard costs for new items).

Different Costing Versions for Planned Costs A costing version for planned costs is primarily used for simulation purposes in manufacturing scenarios. For example, you can calculate the planned costs of manufactured items based on different values for labor and overhead rates, and different values for the item cost records for purchased material.

Other than simulation purposes, the concept of item cost records (within a costing version for planned costs) has limited applicability to items with actual costing as an inventory valuation method. Activating this item cost record simply populates an initial value for the item's actual cost, as displayed in the item master.

Cost Records related to Items The costs for purchased and manufactured items are defined as item cost records within a costing version. However, the use of these item cost records differs between a costing version for standard costs versus one for planned costs. Several rules apply to the item cost records for standard costs, whereas the rules do not apply for planned costs.

This explanation focuses on item cost records. A costing version can contain other types of item-related information, such as an item sales price records and/or item purchase price records. For example, an item sales price record can be automatically created by the cost calculations for a manufactured item, where the calculated sales price reflects a cost-plus-markup approach (Section 5.9).

Cost Records related to Resources and Overheads The hourly costs for a resource (termed *Cost Categories*) and the manufacturing overhead costs are defined as cost records within a costing version. The overhead costs are defined within the construct termed a *Costing Sheet*. These cost records are typically defined in a costing version for standard costs to support standard cost environments. In actual costing environments, these cost records can be defined in a costing version for standard or planned costs. Subsequent sections describe the definition of resource costs (Section 5.5) and overhead costs (Section 5.6).

Comparing Item Costs within Costing Versions The comparison of item cost records depends on your rationale for different costing versions, and how you enter pending costs with a specified activation date. For a selected costing version, you can use the Compare Item Prices report and its associated dialogue to compare the item costs (1) to the pending costs in another costing version or (2) to the active costs as per an effective date. For a set of standard cost data, the report options support calculation of the net change in inventory value.

5.2 Terminology about Item Cost Records and Cost Calculations

Item cost records within a costing version, and the cost calculations for manufactured items, provide the foundation for understanding the use of product costing information. This information is viewed and maintained on several AX forms. However, an explanation using these form names leads to cumbersome English-language sentences.[1] This section summarizes the terminology used in the book and the associated names of AX forms, as shown in Figure 5.1 and described below. The explanation focuses on costing versions containing standard costs, but it also applies to costing versions containing planned costs (which typically do not require activation of item cost records).

---

[1] The form name "Item Price" is one example. The name may have originated because several types of information can be viewed on the Item Price form, such as a calculated value for an item's suggested sales price (aka the item sales price record). However, the name does not indicate the primary purpose of viewing/maintaining information about an item's costs.

Figure 5.1 Terminology for Item Cost Records and Cost Calculations

Terminology used in Book		Name of AX Form
View an Item Cost Record	For a pending cost For an active cost	Item Price
Manually enter an Item Cost Record	For a pending cost	Item Price
Perform a Cost Calculation	For a single item For an item's BOM version For items within a costing version	Cost Calculation for an Item Cost Calculation for a Costing Version
View Results of a Cost Calculation for an item	View an item cost record View costs segmented by cost group View costs in multi-level format	Item Price Summary Calculation Inquiry Complete Calculation Inquiry
Activate Item Cost Record	For a single item For items within a costing version	Item Price Activate Prices

View an Item Cost Record An item cost record defines an item's site-specific costs within a costing version. The initial entry of an item cost record has a pending status, and activating the cost record changes the status to active. Using the Item Price form, you can view both pending and active item cost records for an item.

Manually Enter an Item Cost Record An item's site-specific costs can be manually entered within a costing version (using the Item Price form) to create an item cost record. The initial entry of an item cost record has a pending status, and activating the cost record changes the status to active. Manual entries typically reflect the site-specific costs for a purchased or transfer item, whereas the item cost record for a manufactured item can be automatically created via a cost calculation.

Perform a Cost Calculation for a Manufactured Item (and Create an Item Cost Record) The cost calculation of a manufactured item's site-specific cost creates an item cost record. You can perform the cost calculation for an individual item and a specified cost version, or for multiple items within a costing version. It depends on the starting point for initiating the cost calculation (Figure 5.6).

View Results of a Cost Calculation for a Manufactured Item The results can be viewed for an item cost record on the Item Price form, which provides access to additional inquiries to view costs in a multi-level format or to view costs segmented by cost group.

Activate an Item Cost Record The initial entry of an item cost record has a pending status and pending effectivity date. Activation changes the status to active, and the effectivity date to the actual activation date. You can activate the item cost record for an individual item, or for multiple items within a costing version.

5.3 Significance of Cost Groups

Cost groups serve multiple purposes. Cost groups are user-defined, and you assign them to items, cost categories and overhead formulas. They can support the segmentation (by cost group) of a manufactured item's calculated costs, the calculation of a suggested sales price for a manufactured item based on cost-plus-markup percentages (by cost group), and the assignment of G/L accounts to standard cost variances (based on the cost group assigned to an item). The definition and purposes of cost groups are described below.

Defining a Cost Group and its Cost Group Type A cost group has a user-defined identifier and a designated cost group type. The cost group type indicates the purpose and constrains the assignment of a cost group. The assignment of a cost group type of *direct material* to a cost group, for example, means that the cost group can only be assigned to material items. Figure 5.2 summarizes the significance of a cost group type, and provides examples of cost groups.

A cost group type of *undefined* does not constrain the assignment of a cost group. For example, an item number that represents a subcontracted service may require standard costing, which involves assignment of a cost group with a type of undefined (and a Product Type = Item).

Assigning a Cost Group You typically assign a cost group to purchased items. It may be assigned to manufactured items with standard costing, since the cost group can optionally support segmentation of production-related variances. You also assign cost groups to cost categories and overhead formulas in manufacturing environments. As summarized in Figure 5.2, the cost group type constrains the ability to assign a cost group, such as constraining the assignment of direct material cost groups to items.

Figure 5.2 Significance of Cost Group Type

Cost Group Type	Examples of Cost Groups	Significance for Using the Cost Group
Direct Material	Electrical Fabricated Packaging	The cost group can only be assigned to material items (Product Type = Item)
Direct Outsourcing	Subcontract	The cost group can only be assigned to items identified as a service (Product Type = Service)
Direct Manufacturing	Labor Machine	The cost group can only be assigned to cost categories, which define the hourly costs (or piece rate costs) for a resource
Indirect	Overhead	The cost group can only be assigned to an overhead formula
Undefined	Subcontract *	The cost group assignment is not constrained; it can be assigned to an item, service, cost category or overhead formula.

Legend: * = This approach supports standard costing for an item representing a subcontracted service (Product Type = Item), whereas actual costing must be employed for services (Product Type = Service)

Using Cost Groups for Segmenting the Calculated Costs of a Manufactured Item
Cost groups provide the basis for segmenting and analyzing cost contributions in a manufactured item's calculated costs, such as the cost contributions for material, labor and overhead. Synonyms for cost group segmentation include cost breakdown, cost decomposition, and cost classification. Cost group segmentation serves the following purposes.

◆ Segment costs for different types of material based on the cost group assigned to purchased items. These cost groups represent direct material costs.

◆ Segment costs for different types of resources based on the cost categories assigned to a resource and its operations. Examples include different types of labor and machines, and differences in setup versus run time. These cost groups represent direct manufacturing costs.

◆ Segment costs related to subcontracted services. The cost group is assigned to the item number representing the subcontracted service. Chapter 15 provides further explanation of subcontracted production.

◆ Segment costs for different types of overheads based on the cost groups assigned to overhead formulas. These cost groups represent indirect costs.

◆ Segment costs by cost group type. The cost group type (such as direct material and direct manufacturing) assigned to each cost group provides supplemental segmentation for reporting purposes.

Information about cost group segmentation for a manufactured item's calculated cost can be viewed on the Summary Calculation Inquiry form, Cost Rollup by Cost Group form, and the Variance Analysis Statement report.

Cost groups can serve other purposes related to calculation of a suggested sales price for a manufactured item, and for assigning G/L account to standard cost variances such as a purchase price variance or a production-related variance.

5.4 Overview of an Item Cost Record

The item cost record for each material item is uniquely identified by five key fields. An understanding of these key fields provides the starting point for explaining how to maintain an item's standard cost across time, as described below. However, most of the explanation also applies an item cost record with planned costs. The key fields and other fields in an item cost record are summarized in Figure 5.3 and explained below

Figure 5.3 Key Fields in an Item Cost Record

Field		Significance of the Field
Key Fields in Item Cost Record	Item Identifier	The identifier indicates the item number; it sometimes includes variant codes.
	Costing Version	The costing version can contain standard costs or planned costs; this costing type affects the calculation policies for a manufactured item's calculated cost.
	Site	A standard cost item requires an item cost record for each site that stocks the item. Transfers between sites can result in a variance when standard costs differ.
	Effective Date	Initial entry of an item cost record has a pending status and effectivity date. Activation changes the status (to active) and effectivity date (to the activation date). Activating an item's standard cost record revalues existing inventory if costs change.
	Status	An item's active standard cost record is used for valuing inventory transactions. Pending item cost records are used in Cost Calculations based on effectivity date.
Cost		An item's cost is expressed for its inventory unit of measure. A manufactured item's cost can be calculated or directly entered.
Other Fields		Charges for a manufactured item reflect the calculated amount of amortized constant costs.

◆ *Item Identifier.* The item identifier normally consists of an item number. When the item identifier includes a variant code such as color and size, an item-specific policy (termed *use combination cost price*) determines whether item cost records can be maintained for the various combinations of the item number and variant code(s).

◆ *Costing Version.* A costing version contains cost records for standard costs or planned costs, as indicated by its costing type. The costing type also affects the calculation policies for a manufactured item's calculated cost, since standard costing principles must be enforced for standard cost items.

◆ *Site.* An item's cost record must be defined for each site that stocks the standard cost item. For example, an item purchased (or manufactured) at one site and transferred to a second site will require two item cost records, one for each site. The item's cost at the transfer site can be different, such as an increased cost because of handling and transportation. Transfers between sites when an item's standard costs differ will generate a variance (termed a *cost change* variance).

◆ *Effective Date and Status.* The two fields concerning the status and effective date (also termed the activation date) work together in tandem. The initial entry of an item cost record has a pending status and pending effectivity date. Activation changes the status to active, and the effectivity date to the actual activation date.

A standard cost item can only have one active standard cost record for each site, which will be used for valuing an item's inventory transactions at the site. The concept of one active cost record applies to the item regardless of the associated standard costing version. Activating an item's standard cost record will revalue existing inventory if costs change, and generate a variance (termed a *cost revaluation* variance).

Pending item cost records are used in cost calculations based on their effectivity date, and the future date specified for the cost calculation.

◆ *Cost.* An item's cost is expressed for its inventory unit of measure. A purchased item's cost must be directly entered, whereas a manufactured item's cost can be calculated or directly entered.

◆ *Other Fields.* Price charges -- or *charges* for short -- must be included in an item's cost when the costing version contains standard costs. The primary rationale is that AX employs the charges field to indicate the calculated amount of amortized constant costs for a manufactured item, and the related field (termed price quantity) to indicate the accounting lot size used in the calculations. Ignoring these charges would run counter to standard costing principles.

In terms of purchased items, it is suggested that you enter a zero value for the charges field. The item's standard cost (including charges) is compared to a purchase order price in order to calculate a purchase price variance. You obtain a false variance if you entered a value in the charges field.

You can enter the item cost records and activate individual pending records (using the Item Price form), or activate all pending records within a costing version (using the Activate Prices form).

5.5 Define Resource Costs via Cost Categories

Cost categories define the hourly costs for a resource and its related routing operations. Common synonyms include labor rate codes and machine rate codes. If applicable, a cost category can also define the piece rate for a resource. The cost categories assigned to a resource will act as default values for its operations. The preparation of cost category information includes the assignment of a cost group. Different cost categories will be needed to support different purposes, as illustrated below.

◆ Assign different hourly costs by resource, such as different costs for various types of labor skills, machines, or manufacturing cells.
◆ Assign different hourly costs for an operation's setup and run time.
◆ If applicable, assign piece rates by resource by assigning a cost category to the output units associated with an operation.
◆ Segment different types of direct manufacturing costs in cost calculations, such as segmentation of labor and machine costs, based on the cost group assigned to cost categories.
◆ Provide the basis for routing-related overhead calculations, such as an hourly overhead amount for a resource.

Definition of a Cost Category The definition of a cost category requires two steps: one step to define a *shared cost category* and a second step to define the *cost category* for production purposes.

Define Costs for a Cost Category Each cost category has its associated cost records within a costing version. The cost records can reflect site-specific costs or companywide costs. Cost calculations for a manufactured item employ the current active cost records for a cost category, and also consider pending cost records (based on effectivity date) when using a future calculation date. Figure 5.4 summarizes the key fields in the cost record for a cost category.

Figure 5.4 Key Fields in the Cost Record for a Cost Category

Field		Significance of the Field
Key Fields in Cost Record	Identifier	The identifier indicates the cost category (e.g., labor rate code)
	Costing Version	The costing version type can be standard cost or planned cost.
	Site	The cost record for a cost category can be site-specific or company-wide.
	Effective Date	Initial entry of the cost record has a pending status and effectivity date. Activation of the cost record changes the status (to current active) and effectivity date (to the actual activation date). If an existing record has a current active status, activation changes its status to previous active.
	Status	The current active cost record (regardless of costing version) will be used for valuing the estimated and actual time on a production order. Pending cost records are used in cost calculations based on effectivity date.
Cost		The cost represents a resource's hourly cost (for setup and run time), or its piece rate cost (for output quantity), expressed in the local currency.
Other Fields		The cost group assigned to each cost category provides the basis for segmentation of direct manufacturing costs in cost calculations.

The key fields for a cost category are similar to those of an item cost record, but there are several differences. These differences can be highlighted using an example of a labor rate code. The labor rate can be site-specific or companywide, the labor rate can be different for run time and setup time elements (or piece rate). There is also a slight change in handling the cost record status, where activation of a pending cost record changes its status to current active, and also changes the status of an existing record (if any) from current active to previous active.

5.6 Define Overhead Costs via Overhead Formulas

The definition of an overhead formula supports the calculation of a manufactured item's overheads (termed *indirect costs*). An overhead formula can calculate different types of overheads for a manufactured item, such as material- or routing-related overheads, or overheads based on the item's weight or volume. Each overhead formula has a unique identifier, and it must be defined as part of the Costing Sheet Setup form. After defining the identifier, you can maintain the cost records associated with the overhead formula.

Define an Overhead Formula within a Costing Sheet Setting up the costing sheet involves defining a format for displaying information about the cost of goods manufactured (COGM) for a manufactured item or a production order. The format (termed a *costing sheet*) segments material, labor and overhead costs based on the cost groups assigned to items, cost categories, and overhead formulas.   The definition of a costing sheet format is required to support overhead formulas.   An overhead formula can define different types of overheads, as described below.

◆ *Surcharge Percentage for Material-Related Overhead.* An overhead formula for a material-related overhead employs a surcharge percentage.   For example, the percentage can be applied to the value of an item's first level components that have a specified cost group. Each overhead formula has an assigned cost group.

◆ *Rate Amount for Routing-Related Overhead.* An overhead formula for a routing-related overhead employs a rate amount.   The rate amount will be added to the hourly cost for run time (or setup time) when the operation's cost category has a specified cost group.   Each overhead formula has an assigned cost group.

◆ *Per-Unit Amount based on the Manufactured Item's Weight, Volume or Quantity.* The overhead formula (termed an *output unit based* formula) defines a per unit amount that reflects the specified weight or volume for the manufactured item. It can also simply reflect a per unit amount for a quantity of one. The overhead formula does not employ an assigned cost group.

◆ *Per-Unit Amount based on the Component's Weight or Volume or Quantity.* The overhead formula (termed an *input unit based* formula) defines a per unit amount that reflects the weight or volume for the components of a manufactured item.   Each overhead formula indicates the applicable cost group of the components.

With each of these approaches, you can optionally define applicability rules within the cost records for the overhead formula, so that an overhead formula only applies to a specific manufactured item or group of items.

Key Fields in a Cost Record for an Overhead Formula   You can maintain the cost records for each overhead formula, such as indicating the overheads for different sites, years, and manufactured items.   Figure 5.5 summarizes the key fields in the cost record for an overhead formula.

The key fields for an overhead formula's cost record share some similarities to those of an item cost record, but there are several differences. These differences can be highlighted using an example of a surcharge percentage for a material-related overhead. For example, the surcharge percentage can be site-specific or companywide, and vary by manufactured item based on applicability rules.

There is also a slight change in handling the cost record status, where activation of a pending cost record changes its status to current active, and also changes the status of an existing record (if any) from current active to previous active.

Figure 5.5 Key Fields in Cost Record for an Overhead Formula

Field		Significance of the Field
Key Fields in Cost Record	Identifier	The user-defined identifier assigned to a node within the costing sheet
	Costing Version	The costing version can reflect a cost type of standard cost or planned cost.
	Site	The cost record for an overhead formula can be site-specific or company-wide.
	Effective Date	Initial entry of the cost record has a pending status and effectivity date. Activation of the cost record changes the status (to current active) and effectivity date (to the actual activation date). If an existing record has a current active status, activation changes its status to previous active.
	Status	The current active cost record (regardless of costing version) will be used for calculating estimated and actual overheads on a production order. Pending cost records are used in cost calculations based on effectivity date.
	Applicability Rule	The overhead formula can apply to a specific manufactured item, a subset of items (based on item group), or all manufactured items.
	Overhead — Surcharge Percentage	The surcharge percentage is used to calculate material-related overheads.
	Overhead — Rate Amount	The rate amount is used to calculate routing-related overheads.
	Overhead — Output Unit Based Amount	The per-unit amount applies to the manufactured item's weight or volume, or to a quantity of one.
	Overhead — Input Unit Based Amount	The per-unit amount applies to the components' weight or volume.

Alternative Approaches to Routing-Related Overheads   Several approaches can be used to model routing-related overheads.   One approach involves the just-described overhead formula to calculate an incremental overhead cost for an operation's run time or setup time, or its piece rate.   A second approach employs a secondary resource for a routing operation, where the secondary resource represents a resource overhead.   A third approach applies to situations where overheads can be tied to output units (rather than time), so that the cost category assigned to an operation's output quantity can indicate the overhead amount per unit.

Overhead Costs for Purchased Material   The overhead costs for purchased material often reflect internal handling costs or the costs associated with acquisition, such as duties, freight and other landed costs.   These overhead costs (termed *purchase indirect costs*) can be calculated as a surcharge percentage of the item's value, or as a per-unit amount based on the item's weight or volume.   They are defined within a separate section of the Costing Sheet labeled "Costs of Purchase", much like defining overhead formulas within the Cost of Goods Manufactured section.

5.7 Standard Cost Calculations for Manufactured Items

The cost calculations for a manufactured item will create an associated item cost record within a costing version. The cost calculations require some preparation information about purchased items and manufactured items. The dialogue for initiating the cost calculations varies slightly based on how you initiate them, such as initiating them for a costing version versus a single item. Several policies affect the cost calculations for standard costs, and constant costs will be amortized over an accounting lot size. These topics are included in the following subsections.

◆ Prepare item information for cost calculations

◆ Initiate a cost calculation

◆ Policies affecting standard cost calculations

◆ Amortizing constant costs for a manufactured item

◆ Additional considerations for cost calculations

Prepare Item Information for Cost Calculations Cost calculations use item master information about purchased components and manufacturing items, as described below.

◆ *Information about Purchased Components.* Each purchased component should have an item cost record containing its standard cost. Each component should also be assigned a calculation group and a cost group. The calculation group assigned to a purchased item defines applicable warning conditions in cost calculations (such as zero cost or a zero component quantity for the item). The cost group assigned to a purchased item provides segmentation in the calculated costs of its parent item.

◆ *Information about Manufactured Items.* Each manufactured item should be assigned a calculation group. The calculation group defines applicable warning conditions in cost calculations, such as the lack of an active BOM version. When a manufactured item has constant costs, you should also assign the accounting lot size for amortizing these constant costs, as described in a subsequent subsection.

◆ *Ignore a Component's Costs in the Cost Calculations.* As part of the BOM line information, you can optionally flag a component so that its costs are not included in the cost calculation of its parent item.

◆ *Ignore a Routing Operation's Costs in the Cost Calculations.* You optionally flag a routing operation so that its costs (associated with run time, setup time or piece rate) are not included in the cost calculation of its parent item. These policies are embedded in the Route Group assigned to the operation.

♦ *Treating a Manufactured Item as a Purchased Item.* An item-specific policy will prevent calculation of the item's costs. This "Stop Explosion" policy is embedded in the Calculation Group assigned to the item.

Initiate a Cost Calculation Initiating a cost calculation involves a dialogue, and the nature of the dialogue varies slightly depending on where you initiate it. The cost calculations can be initiated for a single manufactured item or its BOM version, or for multiple items within a costing version, as summarized in Figure 5.6 and described below.

♦ *Cost Calculation for a Costing Version.* Initiating the cost calculation for a costing version will display a dialogue form so that you can enter relevant information. As shown in the right hand column of Figure 5.6, the dialogue inherits the costing version, and you can optionally select items and employ the where-used concept. [2] Information about the specified site and calculation date can be inherited from the costing version policies or manually entered. Figure 5.6 displays the inherited information and the ability to override the information. As an example, the costing version may contain costs for a specified site so that the inherited site cannot be overridden.

You can also initiate the dialogue for a cost calculation by starting from a selected BOM version for a manufactured item.

Figure 5.6 Dialogue for Initiating a Cost Calculation

Dialogue Information	Initiating a Cost Calculation	
	For an Item	For a Costing Version
Item Identifier	Inherited	All items or selected items or where-used items
Costing Version	User specified	Inherited
Site	Inherited from costing version policy; Or manually enter the site and calculation date (if not mandated)	
Calculation Date		
BOM Version	Inherit active version for the item and site; Optionally override with an approved version for the item	Inherit active version for the item and site
Route Version		
Calculation Quantity	Inherit the item's accounting lot size; Optionally override the quantity	Inherit the item's accounting lot size
Calculated Cost	Generate an item cost record for the single item	Generate an item cost record for each selected item

---

[2] The concept of where-used updates is motivated by the single-level cost calculation for standard costs, since an item's recalculated cost can impact higher levels within the product structure. This impact on higher levels can also be calculated by performing the cost calculations for all manufactured items.

Policies affecting Cost Calculations The nature of cost calculations varies slightly depending on whether the calculations involve a costing version for standard costs or planned costs, and the policies that can be inherited from the specified costing version. These policies are explained below.

◆ *Cost Calculation Policies for Standard Costs.* Cost calculations with standard costs must be restricted by costing version policies because the restrictions ensure standard costing principles will produce accurate consistent results. For example, these mandated restrictions mean that cost roll-up calculations are limited to a single level (termed a single level *explosion mode*), the source of a purchased item's cost data must be from the item cost records within a costing version, and charges must be included in the unit cost of an item. Charges for a manufactured item reflect the calculated amortization of constant costs.

◆ *Cost Calculation Policies for Planned Costs.* Cost calculations with planned costs do not have to follow standard costing principles. This means you can perform multi-level cost roll-up calculations, and the source of a purchased item's cost data can be from other sources.

◆ *Other Cost Calculation Policies.* Cost calculations can generate warning messages. For example, a warning message can indicate a zero quantity component or the lack of an active BOM version for a manufactured item.

Amortizing Constant Costs for a Manufactured Item A manufactured item's constant costs reflect operation setup times, or the components with a constant quantity (or constant scrap amount). The concept of an accounting lot size is used to amortize these constant costs in cost calculations. The item's site-specific standard order quantity (for inventory) acts as the default value for the accounting lot size; the quantity may be greater to reflect a multiple within the order quantity modifiers for the item.

The default value for an accounting lot size is displayed as the calculation quantity when performing a cost calculation for a single item, and it can be overridden. The specified calculation quantity only applies to the parent item. An alternative approach only applies to planned cost calculations, where you specify a make-to-order explosion mode so that the specified quantity acts as the accounting lot size for the parent item and all manufactured components.

The calculated amount of a manufactured item's amortized constant costs is termed *price charges (*or *charges* for short*). After calculating a manufactured item's cost, these charges are displayed as two fields identifying the total amount and the accounting lot size (termed the *price quantity* field). These two fields are displayed on the Item Price form. Activating a manufactured item's cost record updates this information on the item master. These charges are always included in the item's standard cost and used for valuing inventory transactions.

Additional Considerations about Cost Calculations   The additional considerations involve the concept of missing costs and use of a fallback principle in cost calculations.

◆ *Calculating costs for items with missing costs.* The concept of a *missing cost* refers to a manufactured item without a pending cost record (for the relevant key fields). A missing cost typically reflects a new manufactured item, or an item that requires recalculation because the pending cost record was intentionally deleted. Cost calculations can be performed for just the items with a missing cost record, thereby supporting a net change approach to cost calculations.

◆ *Cost Calculations using the Fallback Principle.* The fallback principle indicates an alternative source of cost data (for a cost calculation) when an item's cost data does not exist within the specified costing version. Cost calculations for item cost records within a single costing version employ a fallback principle of none. However, several situations can benefit from cost calculations employing a fallback principle of using another costing version or the active cost records.

5.8 Planned Cost Calculations for Manufactured Items

Cost calculations can be used to calculate a manufactured item's planned cost, and create an item cost record within costing version that reflects a costing type of planned cost. Many of the above-mentioned considerations also apply to planned cost calculations, such as the use of cost groups, the two approaches to initiate a cost calculation, and amortizing constant costs

One advantage of using planned costs is that cost calculations can be multilevel rather than single level. A second advantage is the capability to create item cost records for purchased components based on information about each item's purchase price trade agreements, which can then be used for calculating costs for manufactured items. Finally, you can creatively use the fallback principle in planned cost calculations, which minimizes data maintenance for simulation purposes.

Source of Cost Data for Purchased Items There are two basic options on the source of cost data for purchased items. You indicate the choice (termed the Cost Price Model) when performing a planned cost calculation.

◆ *Costing Version* (termed Version Cost Price). Costs for purchased items are based on item cost records within a costing version. These item cost records can be manually entered, or they can be automatically created from purchase price trade agreement information. Automatic creation occurs when you perform the planned cost calculations, and the complete book provides further explanation.

◆ *Calculation Group*. Costs for purchased items are based on the source of cost data designated by the calculation group assigned to an item. In this case, the source of information can be (1) the item's inventory cost, such as the item's actual cost or active standard cost (2) the item master information about the item's standard purchase price, which can be updated automatically by the last purchase invoice, (3) the manually specified cost on the item master, or (4) the purchase price trade agreement information with the item's preferred vendor. The designated calculation group can reflect a companywide policy, which requires the assignment of a blank value for each component item.[3]

A planned cost calculation employs the active cost records for cost categories and overhead formulas. It can also use the pending cost records when using a future date for the cost calculations. The cost calculations generate an item cost record for manufactured items within the specified costing version. This item cost record provides the starting point for viewing the cost calculation details, such as viewing the costs in a multi-level format. This item cost record provides reference information, and is typically never activated.

5.9 Variations of Cost Calculations

A cost calculation can serve different purposes. One example involves the calculation of a manufactured item's suggested sales price with a costing version for standard costs or planned costs. A second example involves an order-specific calculation in the context of a sales quote or sales order.

Calculate a Manufactured Item's Sales Price Cost calculations can be used to determine a manufactured item's suggested sales price based on a cost-plus markup approach or a rolled price approach, as described below.

---

[3] The companywide policy for a calculation group is defined as part of the parameters for Inventory and Warehouse Management.

◆ *Cost-Plus Markup Approach.*   The markup reflects the profit-setting percentages assigned to cost groups, where a cost group can be assigned to each purchased item, cost category and overhead formula. Each cost group can be assigned up to four sets of profit-setting percentages, labeled Standard, Profit 1, Profit 2, and Profit 3.   Within the Profit 1 set, for example, a profit-setting percentage of 50% could be defined for a cost group assigned to purchased material, and a profit-setting percentage of 80% could be defined for a cost group assigned to a cost category for labor operations.

◆ *Rolled Price Approach*   The rolled price approach only applies to a component. The cost calculation uses the component's standard sales price (rather than its cost) to calculate the manufactured item's sales price.

A policy within the calculation group assigned to a purchased item (termed the *sales price model*) determines whether the component's sales price or cost-plus-markup will be used in the calculation of a sales price for a manufactured item.

A cost calculation can generate an item sales price record (rather than an item cost record) within a specified costing version. The item sales price record provides the starting point for viewing the calculation details, such as viewing costs and sales prices in a multi-level format. An item's sales price record primarily acts as reference information. However, activating an item's sales price record will update the item's standard sales price on the item master, which represents one option for an item's sales price.

Order-Specific Calculations for an Item's Cost and Sales Price An order-specific cost calculation typically applies to make-to-order products in the context of a line item on a sales order or quote, and results in a calculated cost and sales price for the line item. It shares many similarities to a cost calculation with planned costs, but it reflects a different purpose and slightly different capabilities.

5.10 Summary of Standard Cost Variances

Several types of standard cost variances can be generated, and each variance will be posted to a relevant G/L account. This section summarizes the variances and definition of G/L accounts.

Purchase Price Variance An item's site-specific standard cost provides the basis for calculating purchase price variances at the time of purchase order receipt (reflecting the difference with the purchase order price) and invoice entry (reflecting the difference between the purchase order price and invoice price).

Cost Change Variance Transfers between sites will generate a cost change variance when there are differences between an item's site-specific standard costs. The variance is generated at the time of receipt for a transfer order. An item's standard cost at two different sites can be different for several reasons. For example, the item's costs may be higher because of the associated transfer costs to another site, or because of different manufacturing or purchasing costs.

Inventory Revaluation Variance Activating an item's standard cost record will revalue existing inventory if costs change, and generate a cost revaluation variance. This variance can also be created when converting to a standard cost model, since conversion of an item's financial on-hand inventory to standard costs will generate a variance for the value difference.

Production-Related Variances Production-related variances are automatically calculated after ending a production order for a standard cost item. The variances reflect a comparison between the reported production activities and the item's standard cost calculation (not to the order's estimated costs). Four types of variances are calculated: lot size variance, production quantity variance, production price variance, and production substitution variance. Similar variances are also calculated for co/by-products. A subsequent chapter about production orders provides further explanation of production-related variances (Section 7.9).

G/L Accounts for Standard Cost Variances Item groups and cost groups represent two factors for the assignment of a G/L account to standard cost variances, such as a purchase price variance or a production-related variance. You define these factors and the relevant G/L accounts on the Posting Profile form.

5.11 Actual Costing Approaches

Several inventory valuation models for actual costing are supported by Dynamics AX, as summarized in Figure 5.7. Each item must be assigned an Item Model Group which defines the inventory valuation model and related policies. An actual costing method (except for moving average) requires an inventory closing process at month end, which settles issue transactions to receipt transactions based on the inventory valuation model assigned to an item. It creates adjustments to the value of on-hand inventory quantities based on financially updated receipts.

Figure 5.7 Actual Costing Methods

Inventory Model	Impact of Inventory Model on the Inventory Closing Process
Weighted Average	Issues will be settled against a summarized weighted average for the month
Weighted Average Date	Issues will be settled against a summarized weighted average for each day
FIFO	Issues will be settled against the oldest receipts within monthly period
LIFO	Issues will be settled against the newest receipts within monthly period
LIFO Date	Issues will be settled against the newest receipts closest to the issue date
Basic Rules for the above Inventory Models	An item's issues will be valued at a running average cost (as of the transaction date). The running average cost reflects the average of the financially updated transactions; it can optionally include physically updated transactions. The user can optionally link (aka mark) a specific receipt to a specific issue transaction.
Moving Average	None. Inventory close only closes the accounting period..

5.12 Additional Case Studies

Case 5.1: Cost Segmentation of Manufacturing Costs A discrete manufacturer calculated the total cost for each of their salable products, and employed cost group segmentation to understand their cost structure. The material costs were segmented into different cost groups (such as electrical parts and fabricated parts) and the manufacturing costs were segmented into different cost groups (such as fabrication, subassembly and final assembly).

Case 5.2: Simulate Impact of Cost Changes The cost accountant at a discrete manufacturer wanted to simulate the impact of potential cost changes on the calculated costs of manufactured items. The company had already been maintaining the active standard costs for all items within multiple costing versions, and the active cost records for labor rates and overhead formulas, so that active cost records could be used as the fallback principle in cost calculations. The cost accountant employed a separate costing version containing planned costs to define pending cost records (for selected items, labor rates and overhead formulas) that represented the potential cost changes, and then performed a cost calculation for this costing version to simulate the impact. The resulting item cost records were analyzed using the Complete Calculation inquiry.

Case 5.3: Allocate Overheads based on Material The cost accountant at a discrete   manufacturer wanted to allocate overheads based on material, especially since routing information was not defined. An overhead calculation formula was employed to apply a surcharge percentage to the value of components in order to allocate overheads to the manufactured items.

Case 5.4: Maintain Standard Costs in Multisite Operations A company produced different end-items at their manufacturing site that were transferred to different distribution sites. In order to maintain the site-specific standard costs, the cost accountant defined multiple costing versions representing the different sites. After calculating the costs of manufactured items at the manufacturing site, these costs were copied to the costing versions that represented the site-specific costs for the distribution sites.

Case 5.5: Calculate Sales Prices based on Cost The sales manager at a discrete manufacturer wanted to calculate a suggested sales price for manufactured items based on a cost-plus-markup approach. The company had already been maintaining a costing version containing the standard costs for all items, labor rates and overhead formulas. The sales manager defined the profit-setting percentages for the various cost groups associated with material, labor and overhead. The sales manager also defined a separate costing version that only contained item sales price records. The sales manager then performed a cost calculation for this costing version to calculate the suggested sales price using a specified set of profit-setting percentages.

Case 5.6: Calculate Sales Prices for a Sales Quotation The sales manager wanted to calculate an item's suggested sales price for sales quotations, which could then be used to support price negotiation efforts. The sales manager wanted the calculated price to reflect a cost-plus-markup approach and the purchase price trade agreements as the source of cost data for purchased components.   As part of entering a sales quotation, an order-specific cost calculation was performed to calculate the suggested sales price, and the suggested price could then be transferred to the sales quotation line item.

Case 5.7: Costing for Precious Metal Components A manufacturing company used several types of precious metal components with purchase prices that could vary widely on a week-to-week basis. They wanted to immediately reflect new purchase prices of the precious metals in each end-item's cost and sales price. Using a standard cost approach, the standard cost of each precious metal was updated after a change in purchase price, and the end-items' costs (and suggested sales prices) were recalculated using cost calculations. The cost changes revalued the existing inventory of components and products, but the company generally carried a minimum level of inventory.

5.13 Executive Summary

Product cost information supports valuation of an item's inventory transactions using a standard cost or actual cost method. Standard costs for items are maintained in a set of standard cost data termed a costing version. Manufacturers can maintain labor rates and overhead formulas in a costing version, and calculate the costs of manufactured items based on BOM and routing information. In addition, the cost calculations can be used for simulating the impact of cost changes, or to calculate a suggested sales price. These simulations can optionally employ a set of planned cost data, which supports additional options in cost calculations. As an example option, the source of cost data for purchased items can reflect purchase price trade agreements rather than the item cost records within a costing version.

With actual costing methods, an item's actual cost is not maintained in a costing version. An item's actual cost reflects financially-updated receipt transactions such as invoiced purchase orders or ended production orders.

An order-specific cost calculation can be used in the context of a sales order, sales quotation or service order line item in order to calculate the estimated cost and sales price of a manufactured item, and optionally transfer the calculated sales price to the originating line item.

Several case studies illustrated product costing functionality, such as cost segmentation for a manufactured item and simulating the impact of cost changes.

Chapter 6

S&OP and Master Scheduling

One of the cornerstones for effective supply chain management in a manufacturing or distribution business consists of effective sales and operations planning (S&OP) game plans. They provide the basis for running the business from the top, and build on the models of the organization's supply chain and decision-making logic. The process typically starts with the definition of all demands for the firm's salable items, and results in S&OP game plans that drive supply chain activities to meet those demands. The nature of an S&OP game plan depends on several factors, such as the need to anticipate demand for an item, the item's primary source of supply, and the need for linkage between a sales order and the item's supply order. Demand forecasts are often used to anticipate demand.

The master scheduling logic within AX plays a critical role in the development and use of S&OP game plans. The term "master scheduling logic" has many different synonyms and the term often varies by ERP software package. Equivalent terms include planning calculations, MRP logic and DRP logic. These planning calculations often reflect one of the more complex aspects of supply chain management and ERP systems.

This chapter reviews common S&OP scenarios in discrete manufacturing and explains the typical business processes to maintain S&OP game plans. It covers key elements of an S&OP game plan such as demand forecasts and sales order promise dates. These considerations are reflected in the following sections within the chapter.

1. Common S&OP Scenarios in Discrete Manufacturing
2. Typical Process to Maintain S&OP Game Plans for a Make-to-Stock Product
3. Overview of Demand Forecasts
4. Safety Stock Requirements

5. Stocked Components for Make-to-Order Products
6. Common S&OP Scenarios with Link to Sales Orders
7. Sales Order Promise Dates and the Delivery Date Control Policy
8. Simulations for S&OP Purposes
9. Guidelines concerning S&OP Game Plans
10. Workspaces related to Master Planning

Master scheduling logic builds on the supply chain model of a manufacturing or distribution business. This includes the fundamentals of modeling inventory locations, the definition of material items, the definition of bills of material and routings for manufactured items, the coverage planning data to model SCM decision making, and S&OP game plans.

6.1 Common S&OP Scenarios

The nature of an S&OP game plan depends on several factors, such as the need to anticipate demand for an item, the item's primary source of supply, and the need for linkage between a sales order and the item's supply order. When demand needs to be anticipated, for example, min/max quantities or demand forecasts often provide a key element of S&OP game plans for stocked end-items or stocked components. The item's primary source of supply may reflect production orders in traditional manufacturing or kanban orders in lean manufacturing, as well as purchase orders and transfer orders in a distribution operation. The need for linkage becomes important for make-to-order and buy-to-order products in order to provide visibility of the sales order demand and for tracking actual costs of goods sold. A given company typically has several major scenarios where each scenario employs different key elements in the S&OP game plans.

The common S&OP scenarios can be broadly grouped in different ways. For explanatory purposes, we'll consider two different groups reflecting the need for linkage between a sales order and an item's supply order. This section covers the first group of S&OP scenarios that do not require linkage. The second group requiring linkage is covered in a subsequent section (Section 6.6).

Several common S&OP scenarios are summarized in Figure 6.1 and described below. For each scenario, the figure identifies the key elements of the S&OP game plan and several additional considerations, including the typical basis of sales order delivery promises. The figure identifies an S&OP scenario for a make-to-stock manufactured item that also applies to a stocked product in a distribution operation, where key elements in the S&OP game plan typically include demand forecasts or min-max quantities. Subsequent sections describe a typical process to maintain the S&OP game plans for make-to-stock products (Section 6.2) and for stocked components of make-to-order products (Section 6.5).

Figure 6.1 Common S&OP Scenarios

	Scenario	Key Elements of S&OP Game Plan	Additional Considerations	Basis of Delivery Promises
No Link to Sales Order	Make-to-Stock End-Item or Stocked Product in a Distribution Operation	Min-Max Quantities	Coverage Code = Min-Max Calculation of minimum quantity	ATP
		Demand Forecast	Coverage Code = Period Forecast consumption by sales orders Using an inventory plan (safety stock)	
		Manual Master Schedule	Coverage Code = Manual or Period	
	Completely Make-to-Order	Sales Order	Coverage Code = Period or Requirement	CTP or CTP via Net Change Explosion
	Make-to-Order End-Item with Stocked Components	Sales Order for End-Item	Coverage Code = Period or Requirement	
		Demand Forecast for stocked components or Min-Max Quantities for stocked components	Coverage Code = Period Forecast consumption by all demands Using an inventory plan (safety stock)	
			Coverage Code = Min-Max Calculation of minimum quantity	

Stocked End-Item based on Min-Max Quantities The simplest S&OP approach employs min-max logic to carry inventory in anticipation of actual demand, where an item's coverage planning policies define the minimum and maximum quantities by site/warehouse. The minimum quantity represents an implied demand forecast, where the quantity typically reflects the daily usage rate multiplied by the number of days for the item's lead time. With min-max logic, when an item's projected inventory falls below its minimum quantity, master scheduling logic will generate a planned order that achieves the item's maximum quantity (subject to an order quantity multiple). The values for an item's minimum and maximum quantities can be fixed, or specified as a pattern (termed the minimum key and maximum key). You can automatically calculate the minimum quantity based on historical average usage over the item's lead time, as described in a subsequent section about calculating safety stock requirements (Section 6.4). Sales order delivery promises can be based on available-to-promise (ATP) logic.

Stocked End-Item based on a Demand Forecast Inventory replenishment based on period lot-sizing logic is driven by the combination of demand forecasts and actual sales orders, which typically involves forecast consumption logic. The number of days for period lot-sizing purposes reflect the desired frequency of delivery, with more frequent delivery of A items (such as daily or weekly periods) compared to B and C items (such as monthly periods).

In addition to the demand forecasts, an inventory plan (expressed as safety stock requirements) can be used to anticipate higher-than-expected customer demand, and meet customer service objectives regarding stock outs, partial shipments and delivery lead times. You can automatically calculate the safety stock requirement based on variations in historical usage and the desired customer service level, as described in a subsequent section about calculating safety stock requirements (Section 6.4).

The planned orders are typically approved (or firmed) in the near term to reflect the desired production schedule and to account for material and capacity constraints. The combination of planned orders and actual production orders represents the item's master schedule, and provides the basis for making delivery promises using ATP logic.

Stocked End-Item based on a Manual Master Schedule The master schedule starts with manually-created planned orders with an approved status, and firming these planned orders results in actual production orders. The item's coverage code can be manual (which does not support net requirement inquiries) or period (where you suppress the action messages). Demand forecasts are not typically entered. This approach avoids the complexities associated with forecast consumption logic, and provides the basis for making delivery promises using ATP logic. Case 6.1 illustrates the use of a manual master schedule.

Completely Make-to-Order End-Item The S&OP game plan consists of actual sales orders for a completely make-to-order product, where CTP logic provides the basis for making delivery promises. Alternatively, delivery promises can reflect a quoted lead time that often represents the item's cumulative manufacturing time. The master scheduling task generates planned supply orders to meet the sales order demand, where the planned orders reflect the item's planning data (such as coverage codes of period or requirement) as well as the active BOM and route versions for manufactured items. This scenario generally implies a pipeline of sales orders with future delivery dates that exceed the item's cumulative lead time.

Make-to-Order End-Item with Stocked Components The use of stocked components can shorten the delivery lead time for make-to-order products, and provide the basis for delivery promises based on CTP logic. Inventory replenishment of these stocked components can be driven by demand forecasts or min-max quantities, as illustrated by the two options in Figure 6.1.

The use of demand forecasts for stocked components involves forecast consumption by any demand, such as dependent demands stemming from production orders for the make-to-order product. An inventory plan may also apply to stocked components, and a subsequent section explains the calculation of these safety stock requirements to meet demand variability.

Another key element of the S&OP game plan consists of sales orders for the make-to-order product. Master scheduling will generate planned supply orders to meet the sales order demand, where the planned orders reflect the item's planning data (such as a coverage code of period or requirement) as well as the active BOM and route versions for the item.

6.2 Typical Process to Maintain S&OP Game Plans for a Make-to-Stock Product

The S&OP game plans for a make-to-stock product often involve a combination of demand forecasts and actual sales orders that drive the item's master schedule, which consists of planned and actual production orders. The term master schedule generally applies to the highest possible stocking level for manufactured items, which consists of saleable items in this scenario. The master schedule provides the basis for making delivery promises on sales orders using available-to-promise (ATP) logic.

A typical business process to maintain the S&OP game plan consists of multiple steps performed by different roles, as summarized in Figure 6.2 and described below. A key role is often called the master scheduler, but this title is not included with the standard AX roles. The master scheduler role typically maintains the game plans and obtains management agreement. This role requires an in-depth understanding of sales and supply chain capabilities, as well as the political power to achieve agreed-upon game plans.

Overview The business process starts with the periodic analysis of historical and projected demands in order to prepare a sales plan and inventory plan for each product, where the sales plan is typically expressed in monthly increments. The inventory plan covers higher-than-anticipated sales order demands to meet desired customer service levels. The master scheduler translates this information into entries for the item's demand forecast and safety stock requirements. After the master scheduling task has been performed, the master scheduler analyzes the results to determine the need for adjustments, and to firm (or approve) planned orders that represent the master schedule. The master schedule provides the basis for realistic promised delivery dates using available-to-promise logic, typically in the context of customer service reps entering sales order lines for the item. In this scenario, actual sales orders consume the item's demand forecast within user-defined forecast periods.

Figure 6.2 Typical Process to Maintain S&OP Game Plans for a Make-to-Stock Product

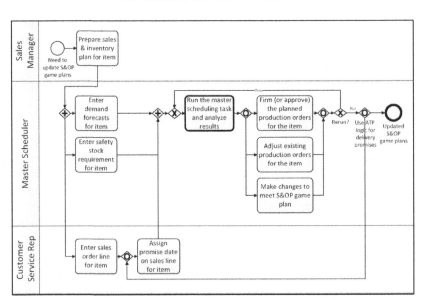

For most scenarios, coverage planning applies to the site/warehouse level, and period lot sizing logic applies to the coverage code assigned to stocked items and their components. The period lot size (expressed in days) represents the frequency of replenishment, and the planned order quantities and dates reflect the time increments and due dates for demand forecasts.

Prepare a sales plan and inventory plan for the item A sales manager role generally has responsibility for analyzing historical and projected demands for the item in order to prepare a sales plan by ship-from location, typically expressed in monthly increments. In many cases the master scheduler must assume this responsibility. The analysis also results in an inventory plan for the item (by ship-from location) to meet the desired customer service levels when actual demands exceed forecast. The analyses may reflect a statistical forecasting technique or some other method.

Enter demand forecast for the item   The master scheduler translates the item's sales plan into entries for demand forecasts, typically expressed in weekly increments (or even daily increments) in the near term. In this scenario, actual sales orders for an item will automatically consume the item's demand forecast within the user-defined forecast periods.

Enter safety stock requirement for the item   The master scheduler translates the item's inventory plan into entries for a safety stock requirement. The safety stock requirements can be entered as a single value, or the value can be calculated based on historical usage. A subsequent section provides further explanation about calculating safety stock requirements (Section 6.4). The safety stock requirements can also be defined as a pattern of multiple values for different time periods.

Run the master scheduling task and analyze results   This activity represents a sub-process with multiple steps and roles. After running the master scheduling task, the master scheduler analyzes the results to identify potential constraints related to material or capacity, and potential problems in meeting demands.   The results include planned orders, action messages, and net requirements for material items, and capacity requirements for resources.

Firm (or approve) the planned production orders for the item   The master schedule consists of the item's production orders, both planned and actual. Planned orders can be approved or firmed, and the suggested quantities and/or dates may be adjusted to ensure a realistic master schedule.

◆ *Approve a planned production order.* By assigning a status of "Approved" to a planned order, master scheduling logic will treat the planned order as if it has been scheduled for the specified quantity and due date. It also locks the BOM/route information (so that planned changes will not be recognized) and prevents deletion when deleting a set of master plan data (unlike other planned orders). An approved planned order must still be firmed to create an actual production order.

◆ *Firm a planned production order.* Firming a planned order generates an actual production order (typically with a scheduled status) for the specified quantity and due date, and also results in the initial assignment of the order-dependent BOM and route information to the production order.

For example, the master scheduler may firm (or approve) the planned orders to represent a level-loaded schedule, or to account for material or capacity constraints. Alternatively, the master scheduler may simply use planned orders to represent the master schedule, and ultimately firm them just prior to starting production. This alternative approach assumes the planned orders reflect the anticipated master schedule.

Adjust existing production orders for the item   The master scheduler may adjust existing production orders to reflect the master schedule, such as changing the quantity or due dates.

Make changes to meet the S&OP game plan   The master scheduler may need to coordinate several types of changes to meet the master schedule. For example, the changes often involve working with purchasing agents to expedite purchase orders for components, or working with production supervisors to adjust capacity or schedules. The changes may also involve working with customer service representatives to delay the promised delivery date on sales orders. These changes often involve trade-offs between conflicting objectives.

Enter sales order line for item   The customer service rep enters sales orders for the item, where each sales line indicates a quantity, ship-from location, and a requested ship date and delivery date. Based on forecast consumption logic, the actual sales orders for an item will automatically consume the item's demand forecast within the forecast period.

Assign promise date on sales line for the item   When the customer service rep creates a sales order line for the item, the earliest possible dates for shipment and delivery are automatically assigned based on available-to-promise (ATP) logic. The ATP logic reflects the master schedule for the item, which helps align actual sales orders to the S&OP game plans. The customer service rep can view available to promise information to answer questions about availability, or disable the delivery date control logic to assign an unrealistic promise date. A subsequent section provides further explanation of the delivery date control logic, and the assignment of requested and confirmed dates to a sales order line (Section 6.7).

6.3 Overview of Demand Forecasts

Demand forecasts often represent one of several key elements in the business process to maintain S&OP game plans. However, a comprehensive explanation about the use of demand forecasts falls outside the scope of an essential guide. This section provides an overview of demand forecasts, starting with the identifier for a set of forecast data and how to enter a demand forecast for an item. It also summarizes the basics of forecast consumption logic, and the options to calculate demand forecasts based on historical data.

Forecast Models and the Identifier for a Set of Forecast Data A set of forecast data has a user-defined identifier termed a forecast model. You specify the forecast model identifier when entering the forecasted quantities and dates for an item. You also specify the relevant forecast model for use in the master scheduling task. Different sets of forecast data can be identified by different forecast model identifiers, but we'll focus on the forecast model containing the current forecast continuously updated as part of the S&OP game plans. A commonly-used identifier for the forecast model is *Current-Forecast* or simply *Forecast*.

Entering a Demand Forecast for an Item Each forecast entry minimally consists of the forecast model, the item identifier, quantity, date, and ship-from site/warehouse. All of the forecast entries with the same forecast model comprise a set of forecast data. Other approaches to entering a demand forecast require additional information, such as forecasts by customer, forecasts for a group of items, and translating monthly or weekly demand forecasts into daily increments.

Basics of Demand Forecast Consumption The combination of demand forecasts and actual demand must be considered to avoid doubled-up requirements for an item. These considerations are commonly termed forecast consumption logic. A basic choice concerns the reduction principle option within the master plan policies for the current master plan, and standard AX supports four major options. This explanation covers the dominant option, where sales orders consume demand forecasts within monthly time buckets.[1]

This option is easiest to explain using a reduction key comprised of fixed monthly time buckets and weekly increments of demand forecasts, which also represent dominant business practices. In this example, any sales orders with ship dates within a monthly time bucket will consume the item's demand forecasts within the same monthly bucket, starting with the earliest unconsumed forecast and consuming forward. The demand forecasts within a given month can be over-consumed; there is no carry-forward effect to consume forecasts within a future forecast period. Changing the sales order ship date to another month (especially the confirmed ship date) will consume demand forecasts in the relevant month.

---

[1] In AX terminology, this option consists of a reduction principle of *Transactions - Reduction Key*, and the option requires two related policies for an item. One of these policies indicates the applicable reduction key, which defines the time buckets for forecast reduction purposes. The second "Reduce Forecast By" policy indicates whether sales orders or all types of demands should consume the demand forecasts.

Calculate Demand Forecasts based on Historical Data Some scenarios can benefit from the calculation of demand forecasts based on sales history information. Standard AX functionality supports the calculation of statistical forecasts, and the approach differs between the AX 2012 R3 version and the new Dynamics AX.

◆ *Calculate Demand Forecasts in AX 2012 R3.* This version introduced one approach to the calculation of demand forecasts, where the forecast models in Microsoft SQL Server Analysis Service are used to create predictions. You can review and adjust these calculated forecasts within an Excel spreadsheet, and upload them automatically into the demand forecast tables within AX.

◆ *Calculate Demand Forecasts in the new Dynamics AX.* Demand forecasts are calculated using the Microsoft Azure Machine Learning cloud service. The service performs best match model selection and offers key performance indicators for calculating forecast accuracy

6.4 Safety Stock Requirements

Safety stock represents a key element in S&OP game plans for those scenarios with stocked products. Within AX, an item's safety stock requirement is defined by the minimum quantity field. You can manually enter a value, or calculate a proposed minimum quantity based on an item's historical usage and its lead time.[2] The significance of the minimum quantity differs between two major approaches for solving S&OP scenarios with stocked items. One approach employs the minimum quantity as part of min-max logic. The second approach employs the minimum quantity to represent an inventory plan in combination with demand forecasts. The inventory plan covers demand variability to meet the desired customer service level in order to reduce stock outs, partial shipments, and delivery lead times.

Standard AX functionality supports the calculation of a proposed minimum quantity based on an item's historical usage, either for min/max purposes or for inventory plan purposes to cover demand variability. An item's historical usage reflects all issue transactions during a specified time period, including sales order shipments, inventory adjustments and other issue transactions. The calculations also identify the impact of the proposed minimum quantity on inventory value, and the change in inventory value relative to the current minimum quantities. A printed report summarizes the impacts on inventory value for all items included in the calculations.

---

[2] The calculation of a safety stock quantity reflects an item's fixed lead time. The assignment of these lead times was previously described for manufactured items (Section 2.4).

You perform these calculations using the Item Coverage Journal form and its related form for journal lines (termed the Item Coverage Journal Lines form). These are commonly referred to as the Safety Stock Journal, and the terms Safety Stock Journal and Item Coverage Journal can be used interchangeably.

6.5 Stocked Components for Make-to-Order Products

Stocked components can support shorter delivery lead times for make-to-order products. The make-to-order product may have a standard BOM and routing, or it may represent a configured item with a BOM/routing defined by a configuration technology. Demand forecasts for these stocked components provide one approach to drive replenishment, but the approach requires the correct forecast consumption logic to avoid doubled-up requirements.

Demand Forecasts for a Stocked Component The entries of demand forecasts for a stocked component are just like demand forecasts for saleable items. The key difference involves forecast consumption logic, so that the demand forecasts will be consumed by any type of demands (also termed issue transactions) within a forecast period. In addition to sales order demand, the demand forecasts for components will be consumed by dependent demands stemming from planned or actual production orders for the make-to-order products. The demand forecasts can also be consumed by transfer requirements to a different warehouse stemming from planned or actual transfer orders. This approach avoids doubled-up requirements when using demand forecasts for stocked components.

To support this forecast consumption logic, the item representing the stocked component must have a "Reduce Forecast By" policy of "All Transactions" rather just "Sales Orders", as defined within the coverage group assigned to the item. This policy works in combination with the selected option for a reduction principle, typically with use of a reduction key (such as monthly time buckets).

S&OP Game Plans for Make-to-Order Products with Stocked Components Demand forecasts for stocked components often represent one of several key elements in the business process to maintain S&OP game plans for a make-to-order product. In a common scenario, the combination of demand forecasts and actual demands for a stocked component drive the item's replenishment. In addition, the stocked components are considered by capable-to-promise logic when making delivery promises on sales orders.

The master scheduler determines which components should be stocked, and works with the sales manager to analyze the projected requirements. These projected requirements must be translated into entries for demand forecasts and safety stock requirements. The master scheduling task generates planned orders for the stocked components, and the master scheduler can approve (or firm) these planned orders as part of the S&OP business process. After entering a sales order line for a make-to-order product, the associated production order can be generated as a planned order by the master scheduling task, or created from the sales order line in order to provide linkage between orders. Figure 6.3 illustrates a typical process to maintain the S&OP game plans for a make-to-order product with stocked components.

Figure 6.3 Typical Process to Maintain S&OP Game Plans
for a Make-to-Order Product with Stocked Components

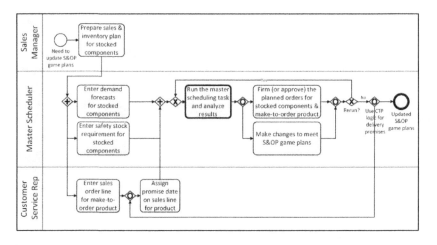

6.6 Common S&OP Scenarios with Link to Sales Order

Some S&OP scenarios involve make-to-order or buy-to-order products that require linkage between a sales order and the item's supply order. An additional type of linkage applies to make-to-order components. These scenarios are summarized in Figure 6.4 and described below. For each scenario, the figure identifies the key elements of the S&OP game plan and several additional considerations. These considerations include creation of the supply order, the suggested coverage code, automatic marking, and the typical basis of sales order delivery promises.

Make-to-Order Product with Link between the Sales Order and Production Order A make-to-order production strategy often involves linking a production order to the sales order line, thereby providing visibility of the sales order demand in production. The reference fields for each order display this link. The basis for establishing this linkage builds on AX functionality for marking. The marking functionality simply provides visibility of the linkage for standard cost items. With actual cost items, marking supports additional functionality to override the suggested matching of a receipt (such as the production order) to an issue (such as the sales order).

Figure 6.4 Common S&OP Scenarios
with Link to Sales Order

Scenario	Key Elements of S&OP Game Plan	Additional Considerations	Automatic Marking	Basis of Delivery Promises
Make-to-Order or **Configure-to-Order** **Product**	Sales Order for the product	Create production order from the sales order line	Yes	CTP or CTP via Net Change Explosion
		Firm the planned production order stemming from sales demand Coverage Code = Requirement	Marking Policy = Yes	
with **Stocked Components**	Demand Forecast or Min-Max Quantities for stocked components	Coverage Code = Period or Min-Max Calculation of minimum quantity	Marking Policy = No	
with **Make-to-Order Components**	Reference Orders for pegged supply components	Auto-create the production order Coverage Code = Period or Req	Yes	

(left vertical label: With Link to Sales Order)

Two basic approaches can be used to create this linkage. As shown in Figure 6.6, the first approach involves creating the production order from the sales order line, which results in automatic marking. The second approach involves firming the planned production order that stems from the sales order demand, which requires the "update marking" policy as part of the firming dialogue.

The linkage between a sales order and production order can be considered a soft link, since changes to the sales order quantity or date do not automatically update the production order. When attempting to delete the sales line, a message displays a warning about the linked production order, and a separate step must be taken to delete the production order. Conversely, deleting the production order removes the linkage and does not impact the sales line. If applicable, a new production order can be created for the sales line.

Make-to-Order Product with Stocked Components The use of stocked components can shorten the delivery lead time for make-to-order products, as described in the previous section.

Make-to-Order Components with Linkage between Production Orders A make-to-order component may be employed in a make-to-order product, where the production order for the component is tightly linked to the parent item's production order. Within AX, you designate the make-to-order component with a line type of "pegged supply" in the BOM or formula for the parent item. The production order for the parent item automatically generates a linked order (termed a reference order) for each make-to-order component. The linkage is identified by the reference fields for each production order, and also by marking information. This linkage is slightly different then the linkage between a sales order and production order, and reflects much tighter linkage between the production orders. Case 3.1 illustrates the use of linked orders.

6.7 Sales Order Promise Dates and the Delivery Date Control Policy

Realistic promise dates for sales order shipments and deliveries can help improve customer satisfaction and supply chain coordination. The initial assignment of the promise dates should align with the item's S&OP game plan, and a sales line with an unrealistic promise date should be highlighted as an exception requiring follow up. After initial assignment, the dates should be changed to reflect changes in the situation, such as changing dates to reflect customer requests or projected delays. Sales orders with unrealistic or past due dates will negatively impact the usefulness of an item's S&OP game plan and the coordination of supply chain activities. The section focuses on promise dates for sales orders in traditional manufacturing scenarios.[3] A similar-yet-different set of policies apply to promise dates for transfer orders.

The initial assignment of sales order promise dates can be supported using several different approaches that reflect a delivery date control policy. The three major options for a delivery date control policy are labeled *ATP, CTP* and *Sales Lead Time*, and the relevant option depends on the scenario and S&OP approach. All three options enforce basic rules to help ensure realistic promise dates. A fourth option (labeled *None*) will disable enforcement of the basic rules, thereby allowing assignment of unrealistic dates. This fourth option is also referred to as disabling delivery date control.

This section starts with a brief background about the sales order dates for shipment and delivery, and the basic rules for delivery date control, and then summarizes the options for the delivery date control policy.

---

[3] In lean manufacturing scenarios, a slightly different approach for delivery promises (based on CTP logic) applies to sales orders for make-to-order products and the generation of sales event manufacturing kanbans.

Sales Order Dates for Shipment and Delivery A sales order header has a requested ship date and a requested delivery date, where the difference represents the transportation time between the ship-from warehouse and the delivery address. It also has a confirmed ship date and confirmed receipt date. A similar set of these four dates applies to each sales order line, and (if applicable) the delivery schedule lines for a sales order line. The dates on a sales order header can be initially inherited by the sales lines, and changes in the header dates can optionally change the dates on sales lines.

Several basic rules can be enforced for the shipment and delivery dates on a sales order header and for each line item, but only when you assign one of major options for delivery date control. The option for a sales order header is inherited from a companywide value, which typically reflects a value of "Sales Lead Time" to enforce basic rules. The option for each sales line is inherited from an item-specific value, where the option should reflect the S&OP approach for the item.[4]

Basic Rules for Delivery Date Control Several basic rules can be enforced for the shipment and delivery dates on a sales order header and for each line item, but only when you assign one of the three major options for delivery date control. The following basic rules apply when initially entering a sales order header or line item, and also when entering changes such as a different date, quantity, ship-from location or ship-from address.

◆ *Calendar for the ship-from warehouse.* The calendar assigned to the ship-from warehouse determines the working days when items can be shipped.

◆ *Calendar for the customer receiving point.* The calendar assigned to the customer (or the applicable customer address) determines the working days when items can be received.

◆ *Transportation time to customer.* The number of days for transportation time can be specified for the different combinations of the ship-from warehouse, the delivery address characteristics (such as the country, state, county or ZIP code), and the mode of delivery (such as air or truck).

◆ *Calendar for mode of delivery.* A calendar can be assigned to various modes of delivery for the ship-from warehouse, where the calendar determines the working days when items can be transported. For example, a truck route may only occur on Thursdays.

---

[4] You define the item-specific option for delivery date control (inherited by a sales line) as part of the Default Order Settings or Site-Specific Order Settings for a saleable item.

◆ *Order entry deadlines for taking sales orders.* The concept of an order entry deadline means that orders received after a specified time are treated as if they were received the next day. You define a set of deadlines for each day within a week (termed an order entry deadline group), and then assign the deadline group to each customer and site.

◆ *Sales lead time.* A sales lead time can represent the number of days to prepare a stocked item for shipment (such as a value of 0 or 1 day), or it can represent the quoted lead time for a buy-to-order or make-to-order product. It will be automatically reflected in the shipment date when using any of the three major options. The number of days for sales lead time is specified as a companywide value, and it can be defined as item-specific overrides.[5]

Delivery Date Control Options for a Sales Order Line A delivery date control option applies to each sales line, and it is initially inherited from the option assigned to the item. The four options are summarized in Figure 6.5 along the typical scenario. For example, the option for ATP (Available To Promise) is typically assigned to a stocked item, whereas the option for CTP (Capable To Promise) is typically assigned to a buy-to-order or make-to-order item.

Figure 6.5 Delivery Date Control Options for a Sales Order Line

Delivery Date Control Option	Scenario	Comments
Sales Lead Time	Use Basic Rules or Quoted Lead Time	Enforce basic rules for assignment of dates
ATP	Stocked End-Item	Enforce basic rules and use ATP logic for dates Analyze supplies using ATP form
CTP	Make-to-Order or Buy-to-Order End-Item	Enforce basic rules and use ATP logic for dates
None	Allow assignment of unrealistic dates	Ignore basic rules for assignment of dates

---

[5] As an alternative approach, the number of days for sales lead time can be defined within sales trade agreements, so that an applicable sales line (for the customer and item) inherits the sales lead time as well as the sales price or discount.

◆ *Using the Sales Lead Time Option.* This option enforces the basic rules for the assignment of dates. In some scenarios, the number of days for "sales lead time" can represent a quoted lead time for the item.

◆ *Using the ATP Option.* This option typically applies to stocked items, where ATP logic focuses on just the salable item. It enforces the basic rules and employs ATP logic for assignment of dates. The ATP option requires several additional policies about underlying assumptions in order to correctly calculate an available-to-promise date. You can analyze the Available Ship and Receipt Dates form, and optionally transfer a selected set of dates to change either the requested dates or the confirmed dates for the sales line.

◆ *Using the CTP Option.* This option typically applies to a make-to-order or buy-to-order item. It enforces the basic rules and employs CTP logic for assignment of dates. The CTP option considers available inventory and receipts for the salable item (if applicable), and automatically results in a net change explosion when needed.

◆ *Using the None Option.* Assigning an option of *none* will disable the rules for delivery date control, thereby allowing assignment of unrealistic dates. As a general guideline, any sales line with this option should be highlighted as an exception or alert requiring follow up.

As an alternative approach, you can initiate a net change explosion for a sales line for calculating a ship date, and it only works when the item's coverage code is other than Manual. You can optionally transfer the calculated date to the confirmed ship date.

Continuous Checking of Sales Order Promise Dates The concept of continuously checking the sales order promise dates is embedded in the messages about a calculated delay generated by the master scheduling task. That is, the message indicates when a sales order ship date cannot be met, and identifies the projected ship date.

6.8 Simulations for S&OP Purposes

A common approach to simulation involves a different set of forecast data with a different forecast identifier. For example, you may define best-case and worst-case scenarios about expected demand with two different forecast identifiers and associated demand forecasts. This forecast identifier is specified as one of the policies for a forecast plan, so that the forecast schedule task can generate a set of forecast plan data. You select the forecast plan data when viewing displayed data about material and resource requirements.

Another common simulation approach involves a focus on just sales order demand, where you indicate the master plan policy to ignore demand forecasts. Examples of other master plan policies that support simulations include the following.

◆ *Time fences for forecasts, coverage and explosion.* The time fences may reflect a long-term time horizon for long range planning.

◆ *Capacity time fence.* The time fence may reflect a long-term horizon for capacity planning purposes. Alternatively, with a capacity time fence of zero, the fixed lead times for manufactured items will be used by master scheduling logic.

◆ *Infinite versus finite capacity viewpoint.* A master plan with infinite capacity planning can be used to identify overloaded periods, so that available capacity could be adjusted via the calendars assigned to resources.

6.9 Guidelines Concerning S&OP Game Plans

Effective game plans lead to improved firm performance and bottom line results. Metrics include reductions in stock-outs, delivery lead time, missed shipments, partial shipments, and expediting efforts. Metrics also include improvements in customer service. The lack of effective game plans is typically cited as a leading cause of poor ERP system implementations. The following guidelines provide suggestions for improving the effectiveness of S&OP game plans.

Minimum Planning Horizon for Each Game Plan   A saleable item's cumulative lead time represents the minimum horizon for a game plan, and additional months provide visibility for purchasing and capacity planning purposes. This minimum planning horizon should be reflected in the item's time fences, such as the coverage and forecast time fences.

Reviewing and Updating Game Plans   The process for reviewing and updating each game plan should be embedded into the firm's regularly scheduled management meetings focusing on demands and supply chain activities. An agreed-upon game plan reflects a balance of conflicting objectives related to sales, engineering, manufacturing, inventory, purchasing and accounting. Periodic revisions to game plans should be reflected in updated forecasts and promised delivery dates.

Primary Responsibility for Maintaining Game Plans   The person(s) acting as a master scheduler typically maintains the game plans and obtains management agreement. This role requires an in-depth understanding of sales and supply chain capabilities, as well as the political power to achieve agreed-upon game plans. The responsibility for providing information about demand forecasts and inventory plans typically belongs to the sales function, with a hand-off to the master scheduler. However, this responsibility is sometimes assigned to the master scheduler. The master scheduler's responsibility for an item's game plans is often identified by the buyer group assigned to the item. .

Formulating Realistic Game Plans   Realistic game plans require identification of capacity and material exceptions that would constrain the plans, and then eliminating the constraints or changing the plan. Identification of material-related exceptions typically starts with suggested actions, while capacity exceptions are identified using work center load analysis. In many cases, a realistic game plan must anticipate demands and demand variations via forecasts and inventory plans for stocked material. Finite scheduling can also contribute to a realistic game plan.

Enforcing Near-Term Schedule Stability   Near-term schedule stability provides one solution for resolving many conflicting objectives, such as improving competitive efficiencies in purchasing and production and reducing exceptions requiring expediting. It provides a stable target for coordinating supply chain activities and removes most alibis for missed schedules. Near-term schedule stability can benefit from inventory plans and realistic order promises about shipment dates. It involves a basic trade-off with objectives requiring fast response time and frequent schedule changes. The critical issue is that management recognizes the trade-offs to minimize near-term changes. An item's freeze time fence represents one approach to support near-term schedule stability, since master scheduling logic will not suggest planned orders during the frozen period.

Making and Maintaining Realistic Sales Order Promises   Realistic delivery promises represent the key link between sales commitments and supply chain activities. You can calculate a realistic promised delivery date during order entry, and also through master scheduling logic and messages that indicate a projected delay in delivery. A key aspect of promised delivery dates is to reduce and isolate the number of exceptions requiring expediting. When available inventory only partially satisfies the sales order requirement, one solution approach involves splitting delivery across two sales order line items (or delivery lines) with different shipment dates.

Executing Supply Chain Activities to Plan   Master scheduling logic makes an underlying assumption that everyone works to plan, and provides coordination tools to communicate needed action. For example, it is assumed that procurement will ensure timely delivery of purchased material so that manufacturing can meet production schedules. It is assumed that distribution will make on-time shipments, and that valid delivery promises were made by sales. An unmanageable number of exceptions will impact this underlying assumption and the usefulness of coordination tools.

Reducing Exceptions that Require Expediting The intent of near-term schedule stability, valid delivery promises and shipment dates, realistic game plans, and executing to plan is to reduce the number of exceptions to a manageable level. This improves the usefulness of coordination tools to meet the S&OP game plans.

6.10 Workspaces Related to Master Planning

The Master Planning workspace summarizes several aspects of information about a selected set of master plan data, including planned orders, action messages, and messages about calculated delays.

◆ *Planned Orders.* You can view existing planned orders, analyze an item's requirements profile or supply schedule, and firm (or approve) a planned order. You can also edit a planned order or manually create a planned order.

◆ *Action Messages.* You can view action messages and the action graph, and apply the suggested action.

◆ *Messages about Calculated Delays.* Separate sections enable you to identify calculated delays related to sales order lines, and also to the requirement dates for demand forecasts and safety stock.

6.11 Additional Case Studies

Case 6.1: Manual Master Schedule for Medical Devices A medical device company produced a line of medical devices that required a manually maintained master schedule to reflect the planner's decision-making logic about production constraints. The medical devices required an expensive outside operation for sterilization, where multiple end-items could be sterilized at the same time. The scheduling considerations included a cost-benefit analysis about amortizing the fixed fee for sterilization over the largest possible number of end-items subject to a weight maximum, while still building the product mix for customer demands and avoiding excess inventory. A manually maintained master schedule proved most effective for this case.

Case 6.2: Demand Forecasts for Office Furniture An office furniture manufacturer produced and stocked different end-items based on demand forecasts, and sales order delivery promises were based on ATP logic. Entries of the demand forecasts reflected weekly increments (with start-of-week due dates) over a rolling three month time horizon (which reflected the cumulative manufacturing lead time), and monthly increments for the next nine months. The master scheduler translated the monthly forecasts into the weekly increments and relevant due dates over the rolling three month time horizon. The translation considered months containing 4 versus 5 weeks, and also weeks with less than 5 working days. Forecast consumption logic was based on fixed monthly periods defined by a single reduction key assigned to all items. Sales orders with ship dates in a given month consumed the demand forecasts within the month. As time moved forward, the weekly increments of unconsumed forecast became past-due and were ignored by master scheduling logic.

Case 6.3: Electric Motors built from Stocked Components   A
manufacturer of standard electric motors produced end-items based on a pipeline of sales orders, where sales order delivery dates were initially assigned based on CTP logic. The motors were built from stocked components in order to shorten delivery lead times. Replenishment of these long lead-time components was driven by demand forecasts. In this scenario, the demand forecasts were defined for an item allocation key, which identified the stocked components and a mix percentage of their typical usage. The demand forecasts were entered in weekly increments over a 3-month rolling time horizon and monthly increments thereafter.

Case 6.4: Demand Forecasts with No Forecast Consumption Logic
A manufacturing company produced standard products based on actual sales orders. The limited forward visibility of these sales orders meant that demand forecasts for end-items were used to drive replenishment of long lead time materials. The master scheduler avoided any confusion in forecast consumption logic by using a reduction principle of none. He maintained the demand forecasts so that they represented the incremental demand that will be added to sales order demands.

Case 6.5: Stocked End-Items in a Distribution Network   A
manufacturing company had a distribution network consisting of a manufacturing plant, regional distribution centers and selling locations. An end-item's inventory was stocked at a distribution center, and then transferred to a selling location to meet actual sales order demand. In this scenario, they entered the item's demand forecasts for each distribution center, and the transfer order requirements consumed the demand forecasts. This required the correct forecast consumption logic. That is, the coverage group assigned to the item and the warehouse representing a distribution center had a "Reduce Forecast By" policy of "All Transactions" rather just "Sales Orders".

Case 6.6: S&OP Simulations   A manufacturer employed simulations to assess the impact of changing demands and supplies. Using multiple sets of forecast data to represent various scenarios, and a designated set of forecast data for planning calculation purposes, the management team could analyze the impact of changing demands on material and capacity requirements.   For example, the master scheduling task was first performed using infinite capacity planning to anticipate overloaded periods. After adjusting available capacity and consideration of alternate routings, the master scheduling task was performed again using finite capacity to highlight unrealistic delivery dates.

Case 6.7: Improve Near-Term Stability in the Master Schedule   A manufacturing company wanted to enforce near-term stability in the master schedule, thereby gaining production efficiencies and reducing exceptions requiring expediting.   They tracked the requested changes to this near-term schedule, and the reasons for each request, and the master scheduler (plus a team of other key people) formally approved or rejected each requested change. An analysis of the requested changes and their reasons provided the basis for improving the near-term stability and the associated benefits.

6.12 Executive Summary

The ability to run the company from the top requires a sales and operations planning process that formulates an S&OP game plan for each saleable product. The nature of an S&OP game plan depends on several factors, such as the need to anticipate demand for the item, the item's primary source of supply, and the need for linkage between a sales order and the supply order.

The starting point for each game plan typically involves identifying all sources of demand such as sales orders and forecasts. Master scheduling logic helps formulate and analyze the S&OP game plans. Realistic promise dates for sales orders can be based on the S&OP game plans and delivery date control policies. Unrealistic promises can be highlighted by disabling the delivery date control logic, and the exceptions should require follow-up.

Several scenarios illustrated how to maintain S&OP game plans, and guidelines were suggested to improve S&OP game plans.   Case studies highlighted variations in the use of S&OP game plans, such as a manually maintained master schedule, demand forecasts for stocked components, and S&OP simulations.

Chapter 7

Production Order Processing

Production orders provide a key coordination tool for scheduling and reporting production activities in most discrete manufacturers. Some mixed mode scenarios also use batch orders and/or kanban orders to coordinate production, but this chapter focuses on the terminology and use of production orders.

A basic model of production order processing provides the starting point for further explanation, such as the order life cycle, the significance of the picking list journal, and other key considerations. It also provides a baseline for explaining variations, such as different approaches to report picking, labor, and finished quantities, and different approaches to coordination of production activities. These topics are reflected in the following sections within the chapter.

1. Basic Model of Production Order Processing
2. Life Cycle of a Production Order
3. Significance of Update Tasks for Production Order Status
4. Key Considerations about Production Order Processing
5. Major Variations of Production Order Processing
6. Considerations for Production Order Picking
7. Options for Labor Reporting
8. Options for Reporting a Finished Quantity
9. Costing for a Production Order
10. Coordinate Production Activities
11. Production Schedules and Capacity Analysis
12. Performance Metrics for Production
13. Workspaces related to Production Orders

7.1 Basic Model of Production Order Processing

The typical steps in production order processing can vary based on several factors, such as different approaches to creation, picking, receiving and inspection. This section summarizes a basic model of production order processing that reflects several simplifying assumptions. The basic model focuses on internal production of a standard product, where a single production order represents one production run and the picking list reflects the entire order quantity. In addition, the manufactured item and its components do not require batch or serial tracking, and the basic model does not include production inspection steps. The basic model provides a foundation for explaining variations in subsequent sections.

Overview of the Basic Model The basic model of production order processing starts with the role of a production planner and a requirement for a manufactured item. The requirement is typically identified by a planned order stemming from S&OP game plans and the item's planning data, and the planned order can be analyzed and firmed to create an actual production order. Alternatively, the planner can manually create and then schedule a production order, typically to meet an unplanned requirement. If needed, the planner reviews and updates the production order prior to reporting the order as released or started.

A machine operator and warehouse worker perform subsequent steps for production order picking and receiving. The steps differ when using the basic versus advanced approach to warehouse management, and the approach can be warehouse-specific. The machine operator can also report actual labor and resources against the production order. The planner updates the order status to Ended when all activities have been reported. These roles and steps are summarized in Figure 7.1 and described below. The figure indicates the two options to report picking and receiving that reflect the warehouse-specific approach to warehouse management.

Firm a Planned Production Order The production planner analyzes and firms a planned production order that reflects requirements stemming from the S&OP game plans and the item's coverage planning data. The production planner can analyze the source of requirements and action messages for the planned order, and optionally edit the planned order -- such as changing the suggested quantity or date -- prior to firming. Firming a planned order results in an actual production order; the actual order is typically assigned an order status of *Scheduled*.[1]

Figure 7.1 Basic Model of Production Order Processing

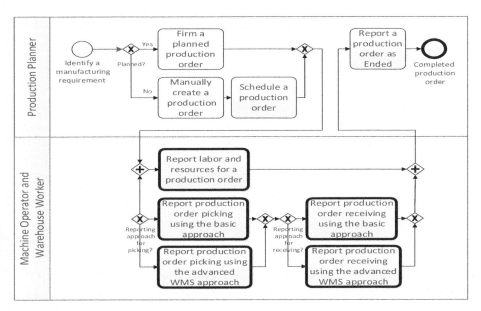

Manually Create a Production Order The production planner manually creates a production order, typically to meet an unplanned requirement. When creating the order (using the Create Production Order dialogue), the planner specifies the item, quantity, site/warehouse and delivery date. Based on this information, the dialogue displays the active BOM version and route version, and these can be optionally overridden prior to order creation. Completion of the dialogue results in the creation of a production order (with a Created status) and an order-dependent BOM and routing.

Schedule a Production Order The production planner schedules a manually-created production order so that the requirements for components and resources will be recognized. The scheduling logic assigns the start/end dates to the production order, and also the operation start/end times when using routing data. This step changes the order status to Scheduled, and it may also be taken for a production order that has already been scheduled. The two choices for scheduling an order – termed operations scheduling and job scheduling -- were discussed in a previous chapter about routing information (Section 4.9).

Review/Update the Production Order   The production planner may need to review and update the production order. For example, the production planner may change the order quantity or the order-dependent BOM, schedule the production order on different dates, or lock the order to prevent rescheduling. When using routing data and job scheduling of production orders, the production planner can review the detailed schedule of operation start/stop times in tabular or Gantt chart format, and optionally assign an operation to a different resource. This step is not shown in Figure 7.1 to keep the diagram simple.

Report Labor and Resources for a Production Order   The need for reporting labor and resources depends on the use of routing data, and the reporting approach can vary. When actual time must be reported, the machine operator can report actual operation time and unit completions, and unit completions for the last operation can optionally update the finished quantity. Some scenarios will auto-deduct labor and resources, which can be triggered by reporting a production order as started or by reporting a finished quantity. The reporting of labor and resource usage provides the basis for calculating remaining work for the production order.

Report Production Order Picking using the Basic Approach to Warehouse Management   The basic approach supports order-based picking for production orders. In a typical process, the machine operator reports a production order as Started which acts as the trigger for creating a picking list journal based on the Start dialogue policies. The warehouse worker reviews the printed version of the picking list journal, reports actual picking against the picking list journal, and then posts it. The picked material is charged to work in process for the production order, and deducted from inventory. In some cases, the machine operator may need to revise actual usage relative to the picked material.   The machine operator manually creates a picking list journal containing the adjustments and then posts it.

Report Production Order Picking using the Advanced WMS Approach to Warehouse Management   In a typical process with order-based picking, the production order is reported as Released which acts as the trigger for several automatic actions. This includes creating and releasing a production wave for the order, which triggers creation of picking work for delivering components to a production input location when it has insufficient component inventory. The warehouse worker reviews the released production waves and the associated picking work for raw material. Using the mobile device, the warehouse worker reports completion of the raw material picking work for delivering components to the designated production input location.

When ready, the machine operator reports a production order as Started, which automatically generates a picking list journal based on the Start dialogue policies. The machine operator reports actual material usage on the picking list journal and posts it. In some cases, the machine operator will manually generate a picking list as an alternative to automatic generation, or to identify unexpected component requirements. In either case, the machine operator posts the picking list journal after reporting actual material usage.

An alternative process employs wave picking, where the contents of a production wave consist of raw material picking work orders that have been created for multiple released production orders. The contents of the production wave are defined by a wave planning process, where some of the steps can be performed automatically to reflect normal decision making logic, as modeled by policies within a wave template. For example, a production wave template might be defined so that the raw material picking work created by releases of different production orders at different times will be automatically added to an existing wave. If needed, the planner can manually update the wave contents (such as adding or deleting wave lines) prior to processing and releasing the production wave. At that point in time, the warehouse worker uses the mobile device to report completion of the raw material picking work for delivering components to the designated production input location.

Report Production Order Receiving using the Basic Approach to Warehouse Management The finished quantity of a production order can be reported using different approaches and delivered to different locations. For example, the finished quantity may be reported multiple times for a given order, or reported once when it represents the entire order quantity. In addition, the finished quantity may be reported into a production location by the machine operator, or it may be reported into a stocking location by a warehouse worker. The machine operator updates the order status to Reported as Finished after all production output has been reported.

Report Production Order Receiving using the Advanced WMS Approach to Warehouse Management The finished quantity of a production order can be reported using different approaches and delivered to different locations. For example, the finished quantity may be reported multiple times for a given order, or reported once when it represents the entire order quantity. The finished quantity can be reported using a mobile device transaction or a client transaction. The machine operator updates the order status to Reported as Finished after all production output has been reported.

The finished quantity of a production order can also be placed in different locations. For example, the finished quantity may be reported into a production output location by the machine operator, and a work order for putaway can be created automatically. A warehouse worker can then use the mobile device for reporting completion of the putaway work order. A single mobile device transaction can also be used to report both the finished quantity and its associated putaway to a location.

Report a Production order as Ended The production planner updates the order status to Ended, which indicates no additional transactions need to be reported. When there are missing transactions, the system provides warning messages and does not change the order status to Ended, although specifying an override will force an Ended status. After ending the production order, the variances are automatically calculated for a standard cost item, and actual costs are calculated for an actual cost item.

Enforce Steps in Production Order Processing Some scenarios need to limit the ability to change production order status, such as preventing a jump to a started status so that orders must be reported as released before they can be started. The ability to enforce or skip steps is determined by companywide or site-specific policies, which consist of a matrix about the allowed changes from one status to another.[2]

Different Approaches to Create a Production Order The basic model identifies two common approaches for creating a production order – by firming a planned order and by manual entry. Several other approaches can be used for creating a production order. For example, you can create a production order from a sales order line (to establish linkage between orders), or the system can automatically create a production order for a make-to-order component (aka a reference order). A production order can also be created from a project. The steps within the basic model also apply to these other approaches to create a production order.

---

[2] The ability to skip steps can be defined as a companywide policy (on the Status Tab of the Production Control Parameters form) or as a site-specific policy (on the Status Tab of the Production Control Parameters by Site form).

7.2 Life Cycle of a Production Order

Several aspects of order status were introduced in the basic model of production order processing. This section summarizes the possible values for order status and related life cycles. It also summarizes the impact of order status on several aspects of system behavior. An in-depth explanation involves the significance of update tasks for changing order status, as described in the next section.

Life Cycles Related to a Production Order The life cycle of a production order consists of several steps and a related order status, as illustrated in Figure 7.2. The steps reflect the basic model described in the previous section. The figure also shows the impact of various steps on the inventory status for the parent and component items   The figure includes the related construct of a picking list journal, but does not include all related constructs in order to keep the diagram simple. For example, it does not include the route card journal (when using routing data) or quality orders (during and after production). Nor does it include several constructs related to the advanced approach to warehouse management, such as the production wave and work orders for raw material picking, and the work orders for putaway of a finished quantity.

Figure 7.2 Life Cycles related to a Production Order

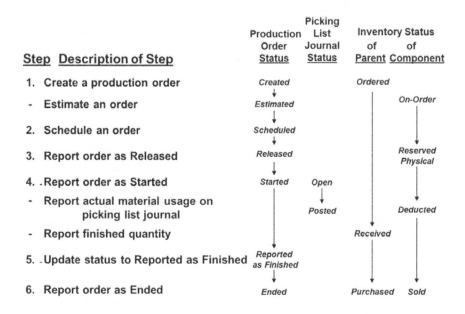

Impact of Order Status on System Behavior The order status affects several aspects of system behavior, as illustrated in Figure 7.3. With an order status of Created, for example, master scheduling logic recognizes the expected parent receipt but does not recognize the requirements for components or resources. The resource requirements will be recognized after updating the order status to Scheduled.   As another example, you can report actual production activities when the order status is Started or Reported as Finished, but not for the Ended status. The significance of order status is closely intertwined with the use of update tasks for changing the status, as described in the next section.

Figure 7.3 Impact of Order Status on System Behavior

Significance of the Current Status		Order Status						
		Created	Estimated	Scheduled	Released	Started	Reported as Finished	Ended
Logic in Master Scheduling	Recognize Expected Parent Receipt	Yes	Yes	Yes	Yes	Yes	No	No
	Recognize Expected Co-Product Receipt	Yes	Yes	Yes	Yes	Yes	No	No
	Recognize Component Requirements	No	Yes	Yes	Yes	Yes*	No	No
	Recognize Operation Requirements	No	Yes	Yes	Yes	Yes*	No	No
	Status Option for Firming a Planned Order	No	Yes	Yes	Yes	Yes	No	No
	Modify Order-Dependent BOM or Routing	Yes	Yes	Yes	Yes	Yes	No	No
	Timing Option for Automatic Reservations	No	Yes	Yes	Yes	Yes	No	No
	Copy BOM or Routing to Order	Yes	Yes	No	No	No	No	No
	Generate Shop Paperwork for Routing Operations	No	No	No	No	Yes	Yes	No
	Create work orders for raw material picking	No	No	Yes	No	No	No	No
	Generate Picking List Journal	No	No	No	No	No	Yes	No
	Report Actual Production Activities	No	No	No	No	No	Yes	No
	Change or Split Order Quantity	Yes	Yes	Yes	Yes	Yes	No	No
	Reset Order Status	N/A	Yes	Yes	Yes	Yes	Yes	No
	Ability to Delete Order	Yes	No	No	No	No	No	Yes

* = Remaining component requirements are ignored after reporting a picking list as completed, and remaining operation requirements are ignored after reporting an operation as completed

7.3 Significance of Update Tasks for Production Order Status

The life cycle of a production order consists of several steps and a related order status.   The order status represents a linear progression that affects order behavior, such as the ability to report actual production activities. The actual reporting of steps in the linear progression can be skipped.   However, the unreported steps will still be performed automatically in most cases. Steps can also be reversed by resetting order status.

Each step involves a user-initiated update task (and an associated dialogue) and the update task can change the order status. For example, changing order status to Started involves a start task and an associated start dialogue, and default values can be defined for many of the dialogue fields. The order status requires an understanding of these update tasks. The types of update tasks and their significance are summarized in Figures 7.4 and 7.5, and explained below. The figures also indicate the ability to define dialogue default values, and the option to include reference orders linked to the production order.

Figure 7.4 Update Tasks for Production Orders

		Significance of Update Task	Dialogue Default Values	Option to Include Reference Orders
Type of Update Task	Create	Initially create a new production order	N/A	N/A
	Estimate	Initially perform (if needed) to calculate material requirements and order costs Perform (if needed) cost-plus-markup calculation of a sales price Perform again (if needed) to recalculate order costs based on updated information	Yes	Yes
	Schedule	Initially schedule material and capacity requirements Perform again (if needed) to reschedule order based on updated information	Yes	Yes
	Release	Perform (if needed) to print shop traveler of routing operations Perform (if needed) to support order scheduling via MES approach Create work orders for raw material picking (when using Advanced WMS approach)	Yes	Yes

Create Order Task The critical information in the create order dialogue includes the item, quantity, delivery date, and the deliver-to site/warehouse. Based on this information, the dialogue displays the active BOM version and routing version, but these can be optionally overridden. Once the order has been created, the order-dependent BOM and routing initially reflect the specified versions, and they can be manually maintained.

Estimate Order Task The estimate order task calculates the order costs based on the order-dependent BOM and routing, the related cost information, and the order quantity. A price calculation inquiry displays the order's per-unit costs. The estimate order task represents an optional step when you need to calculate estimated costs prior to scheduling or starting an order. It is typically performed automatically as a result of updating order status to a higher status such as scheduled or started.

Schedule Order Task There are two scheduling methods termed operation scheduling and job scheduling, as described in the previous chapter about routing information (Section 4.9). The scheduling method is only relevant when using routing data, and the choice depends on how you assign resource requirements to an operation. Job scheduling must be used when resource requirements are defined in terms of resource capabilities or employee competencies, or when you perform detailed scheduling of production resources (e.g., via Gantt charts).

When scheduling an order using either method, you specify the critical information in a schedule order dialogue, such as the scheduling direction and several scheduling policies. The scheduling direction, for example, could be forward from today's date or backward from a specified scheduling date. The scheduling policies can optionally include consideration of finite capacity and material. The schedule order task must be repeated after changing the order quantity or the order-dependent BOM and routing.

You can optionally specify that an order is locked, thereby preventing rescheduling by master scheduling logic or by the schedule order task.

Release Order Task The release order task has three major purposes. First, the release dialogue can be used to optionally print shop traveler paperwork (related to routing information) prior to starting production activities. Second, the information about released orders can be used for adjusting daily schedules when using the MES capabilities for reporting labor. And third, the release order task can generate work orders for raw material picking when using the advanced approach to warehouse management.

Start Task Starting an order quantity (via a start order dialogue) represents an authorization for reporting actual production activities. The relevant information depends on the significance of a single order. In some scenarios, you will start the entire order quantity and all operations. In other scenarios, you will start a partial order quantity or selected operations. You can also indicate completion of all picking activities or routing operations so that master scheduling logic will ignore remaining requirements.

The reporting of actual production activities includes component material usage, time and unit completions by operation, and finished quantities. Unit completions at the last operation can optionally update the finished quantity for the parent item.

Figure 7.5 Update Tasks for Production Orders – Part 2

Significance of Update Task			Dialogue Default Values	Option to Include Reference Orders
Type of Update Task	Start	Indicate started quantity (and selected operations) Generate picking list journal for the started quantity (and selected operations) Generate route card journal for the started quantity (and selected operations) Perform again (if needed) to define additional started quantity (and selected operations) Perform again (if needed) to indicate completion of all picking and/or all operations	Yes	Yes
	Report as Finished	Report receipts, and optionally indicate completed order, picking, or all operations Perform again (if needed) to report additional receipts or indicate completed order Perform again (if needed) to indicate completion of all picking and/or all operations	Yes	N/A
	End	Change status to ended , thereby preventing further transactions Calculate variances for standard cost items, and actual costs for actual cost items	Yes	
	Reset Status	Change order status to created, thereby allowing deletion of order Change order status, thereby reversing all associated transactions	Yes	Yes

Report as Finished Task The report-as-finished task provides one option for reporting finished quantities, as described in a subsequent section (Section 7.8). The finished quantity can be expressed in terms of the good quantity and an optional scrap quantity. The scrap quantity is also termed the error quantity or trashed quantity. As part of the report-as-finished dialogue, you can optionally indicate completion of all picking activities or routing operations, so that master scheduling logic will ignore remaining requirements. The order status changes to Reported as Finished after flagging the order as complete using the End Job flag.

The reported-as-finished status means that the system ignores remaining component/routing requirements and expected parent receipts, but additional transactions can be reported. Order status will not change to Reported as Finished when transactions are missing unless you indicate that errors will be accepted (as part of the report-as-finished dialogue). Missing transactions may include expected parent receipts or remaining requirements for components and operations.

End Task The end task changes the order status to Ended. The end dialogue also indicates how to handle costs associated with a scrap quantity, either by allocating scrap costs to actual parent receipts or by charging them to a specified G/L account. Charging scrap costs to a specified G/L account only works when actual costing applies to the parent item.

Under certain conditions the end task can be performed instead of the report-as-finished task (via the reported-as-finished flag in the end task dialogue), where the system assumes the entire order quantity will be reported as finished.

Reset Status Task   A production order can be reset to a previous status, and you indicate the desired order status on the reset order dialogue. For example, order status may be changed to Created to allow deletion, or changed to Released from started so that the system automatically reverses all transactions about actual production activities.

Update Tasks and the Option to Include Reference Orders   Several update tasks for a production order have an option to include reference orders, as indicated in the right-hand column of Figures 7.4 and 7.5. A reference order reflects a buy-to-order or make-to-order component. The reference orders can be included in cost calculations, scheduling, releasing, and the authorization to start production activities. For example, the estimate task will always generate reference orders, and the schedule order task can optionally include reference orders and even synchronize them. Resetting order status can apply to reference orders. Deleting an order can optionally delete the reference orders. The update tasks can also be performed for a production order that represents a reference order.

The nature of reference orders has been covered in a previous chapter about common S&OP scenarios requiring linkage between orders (Section 6.6). A previous chapter also covered the definition of buy-to-order and make-to-order components in bill of material information (Section 3.4)

7.4 Key Considerations about Production Order Processing

The basic model of production order processing provides the foundation for explaining key considerations and major variations that reflect different ways of doing business. This section describes some of the key considerations and the next section covers major variations. Examples of key considerations include the production order quantity and lead time, locking an order to prevent rescheduling, the use of a stopped flag, and identifying material shortages.

Production Order Quantity and UM   A production order quantity reflects the item's inventory UM. It can optionally reflect order quantity modifiers consisting of a minimum, multiple and maximum. For example, these modifiers are considered in planned orders and when manually creating or maintaining an order. In addition, when creating an order, the order quantity can impact the suggested route version when you have defined quantity breaks for different route versions.

Splitting the Quantity for a Production Order   Splitting a production order results in a new order for the specified quantity and delivery date. The split order quantity must be less than the originating order quantity, and you normally split an order prior to a started status. A started production order can be split, but only for a quantity that has not yet been reported as started. This approach avoids the complications associated with allocations of issued components and reported operation times to the split orders.

Production Lead Time   Scheduling logic can calculate a variable production lead time for planned and actual production orders based on routing data, or use a fixed lead time when no routing data applies. Several factors apply to the calculation of a variable lead time, such as the order quantity, the resource requirements for routing operations, and the available capacity of resources. The uses of a fixed lead time were described in a previous chapter about the coverage planning data for a manufactured item (Section 2.3).

Lock a Production Order to Prevent Rescheduling   A production order can be flagged as locked to prevent rescheduling, and then unlocked when desired.

Assign a Stop flag for a Production Order   The Stop flag primarily serves warehouse management purposes and prevents changes in order status prior to starting a production order. For example, assigning the Stop flag to a scheduled order prevents a change in order status to Released (which prevents creation of raw material picking work) or Started (which prevents reporting of actual material usage). The Stop flag also prevents resetting order status. You assign and remove the Stop flag as an explicit step on the Production Orders form, and a Stop flag is also displayed as part of the warehouse management information for the order. The Stop flag has no impact when raw material picking work already exists, or when assigned after a production order has been started.[3]

Identify Material Shortages for a Production Order   A material shortage represents the remaining requirements for a component in the Production BOM for a started production order. The system ignores the components' remaining required quantity under several conditions: when a specific component has been flagged as completely picked; when picking for all components has been flagged

---

[3] An additional option (within the new Dynamics AX) enables you to assign the Stop flag and unpick the components, which reverses the raw material picking work when using the Advanced WMS approach to production order picking.

as complete; when an operation linked to the material has been flagged as complete; or when the production order status becomes Reported as Finished. Shortages can be viewed on the Material Stock-out List inquiry.

7.5 Major Variations of Production Order Processing

The basic model of production order processing provides a foundation for covering several major variations. The basic model included some of the variations, such as using the basic versus advanced approach to warehouse management for picking and receiving. These two variations are described in subsequent chapters about the basic approach (Chapter 8) and the advanced approach (Chapter 9). Several other major variations merit a separate section, such as the options for production order picking (Section 7.6), labor reporting (Section 7.7), and reporting finished quantities (Section 7.8). This section addresses some additional variations, including the significance of a single order and the picking list journal, scheduling an individual order, production inspection, rework orders, and subcontracted production.

Significance of a Single Order and the Picking List Journal   The significance of a single production order and its related picking list journal(s) can differ widely depending on the scenario. In a simple scenario, for example, the production order represents a single production run and the picking list journal contains all components and reflects the entire order quantity. In other scenarios, the order quantity for a single order may represent multiple production runs within a day or week, and a picking list journal may be created for each production run (and its associated quantity). Depending on the significance of a single order, it impacts the reporting of the started quantity for an order, the automatic generation of picking list journals for the started quantity, the reporting of labor and finished quantities for the order, and the assignment of batch numbers to finished quantities. Subsequent sections describe the options for production order picking (Section 7.6), labor reporting (Section 7.7), and reporting finished quantities (Section 7.8).

The significance of a picking list journal differs between the basic and advanced approaches to warehouse management. In the basic approach, it is used for reporting actual picked quantities and actual material usage. In the advanced approach, it is only used for reporting actual material usage, since work orders are used for reporting raw material picking. Subsequent chapters describe basic warehouse management for production orders (Chapter 8) and advanced warehouse management (Chapter 9).

Link a Production Order to a Sales Order   A make-to-order production strategy often involves linking a production order to the sales order line, thereby providing visibility of the sales order demand in production. The linkage is identified by the reference fields for each order, and also by marking information. Two basic approaches can be used to create this linkage, as described in the previous chapter about common S&OP scenarios (Section 6.6). The first approach involves creating the production order from the sales order line. The second approach involves firming the planned production order that stems from the sales order demand, which requires the "update marking" policy as part of the firming dialogue.

Linked Production Orders (aka Reference Orders)   The production order for a make-to-order component can be linked to the parent item's production order. Within AX, you designate the make-to-order component with a line type of "pegged supply" in the BOM version for the parent item. The production order for the parent item automatically generates a linked order (termed a reference order) for each make-to-order component. The linkage is identified by the reference fields for each production order, and also by marking information.

Schedule an Individual Order   Scheduling an individual production order has several considerations. It can change order status to scheduled, or update an already scheduled order, so that requirements for resources and materials will be correctly recognized and scheduled. The resource requirements and related scheduling logic only apply when using routing data. The considerations include the scheduling method of job scheduling versus operation scheduling (described in Section 4.9), the scheduling direction (of forward versus backward scheduling), and several options for the scheduling logic. For example, the scheduling logic can consider finite capacity and material, and the related reference orders.

Production Inspection   There are several variations of production inspection for the finished quantity of a production order. For example, the inspection may be performed by machine operators at the time of reporting a finished quantity, so that the operator can immediately identify a trashed quantity or assign an Inventory Status such as *To-be-Scrapped* or *Needs-Rework*. Alternatively, inspection may be performed after reporting a finished quantity, where a quality control clerk reports test results against an automatically-created quality order. The test results may be reported while the material remains in a production location, or the material may be placed in a separate QC area until test results have been reported. Validation of the quality order can automatically update the Inventory Status of the finished quantity.

There are also several variations of production inspection at one or more steps in the routing for a production order. For example, a routing operation can identify the resource requirements for an inspector, and/or a quality order can be automatically created by reporting completion of a routing operation. A subsequent chapter about quality management provides further explanation about quality orders and inspection approaches (Chapter 10).

Rework Order for a Finished Quantity Rework may be necessary for the finished quantity of a production order that has not been reported as scrapped. A separate production order can be used to formally manage the rework for an item, where you identify the same item as the parent and a component. More specifically, you manually create a new production order for the item but with an unspecified BOM version, and you add the same item as a component in the Production BOM. The component should also be reserved after updating the order status to Estimated, especially when it represents a batch-controlled or serialized item. The rework activities may involve usage of other component materials, which can be simply issued to the production order, or added to the Production BOM and then issued. After a production order has been created for rework purposes, the remaining steps are exactly the same as the basic model of production order processing.

Some scenarios also track the labor and resources for rework activities. When creating the order, you can indicate an unspecified route version, and manually add at least one operation so that time can be reported against the operation number. The operation typically identifies a master operation that represents rework. Alternatively, you can indicate an approved route version for the item that contains one or more operations reflecting the rework activities.

Subcontracted Production Subcontracted production and internal production share many similarities in the use of basic constructs like production orders and picking list journals. They both employ BOM and routing information. However, subcontracted production involves significant differences and several variations. One key difference stems from the AX approach to modeling subcontracted production, which requires a unique item representing the subcontracted service, and a BOM line specifying it as a buy-to-order component for the manufactured item. As a result, a production order for the manufactured item automatically creates the associated purchase order for the subcontracted service. The routing data for the manufactured item and its production order also includes an outside operation that represents subcontracted production. The dual constructs of a production order and its associated purchase order involve additional complexity in setup information and business processes in comparison to internal production.

Subcontracted production can have many possible scenarios. The different scenarios typically reflect variations of the supplied material and handling of finished quantities, and how these are modeled and reported within AX. Other differences stem from the routing data, since the outside operation may reflect the only operation or one of several operations. An explanation of these variations falls outside the scope of this essential guide, and complete book provides a comprehensive explanation.

7.6 Considerations for Production Order Picking

The business process for production order picking, and the significance of a production picking list, differ between the basic and advanced approach to warehouse management. However, several considerations apply to both approaches. These considerations include the significance of a single order, the Production BOM, the warehouse source of components, reservations for components, the flushing principle for a component item, the variations in generating and posting a picking list journal, and production order picking via auto-deduction.

Significance of a Single Production Order   The significance of a single production order can vary in different scenarios, especially those involving a batch-oriented production process and items with batch tracking. It may represent a single production run (aka physical batch) in some scenarios, or the order quantity may represent multiple production runs within a day or week in other scenarios. Depending on the significance of a single order, it impacts the reporting of the started quantity for an order and the automatic generation of picking list journals for the started quantity.

Production BOM   The Production BOM provides the basis for line items in a picking list journal, and a previous chapter described this order-dependent BOM (Section 3.7). Multiple aspects of a Production BOM impact the generation and use of the picking list journal. For example, the suggested locations on the picking list journal reflect the approach for defining the components' warehouse source and the approach to reservations, and a component's flushing principle can determine when it should be included in a picking list journal.

Warehouse Source of Components   A component's warehouse source indicates where to pick the item when reporting actual usage for a production order. You define a component's warehouse source as part of the BOM and routing information for its parent item, and this information will be inherited by the Production BOM and ultimately by the picking list journal. A previous chapter explained the four major options for defining the warehouse source of components (Section 3.5).

Reservations for Production Order Components The reservation policy assigned to a production order determines when components will be reserved relative to order status. The reservation policy for an order is initially inherited as a companywide or site-specific policy and it can be overridden. In most scenarios, you select a reservation policy so that components will be automatically reserved at the time of releasing or starting the production order. Some scenarios employ a reservation policy of Manual. You can view and update reservations for components in the Production BOM or the Picking List Journal by accessing the Reservations form.

A related reservation policy only applies to the Advanced WMS approach to warehouse management, and it determines whether components must be fully reserved or partially reserved in order to release a production order.

Significance of the Flushing Principle for Populating Picking Lists The flushing principle assigned to a component item provides the basis for populating a picking list journal. For example, a flushing principle of *Start* provides the basis for populating a picking list when you report an order as Started. A flushing principle of *Finish* provides the basis for populating a picking list when reporting finished quantities for an order. A flushing principle of *Manual* typically applies to items that should not be included when generating a picking list.

In order to effectively use the flushing principle, it must be considered in the Start dialogue when reporting an order as Started, and in the Report as Finished dialogue when reporting a finished quantity. As part of the Start dialogue, you can optionally populate the picking list with all components (regardless of flushing policy), or immediately post the picking list (which provides auto-deduction of components).

Variations in Generating and Posting a Picking List Journal Material usage can only be reported through a picking list journal. There are multiple variations for generating a picking list, where the variations reflect differences in modeling the business process. In the basic model, for example, starting a production order generated a single picking list journal for all components, and a manually-created picking list was used for reporting adjustments and corrections. The following examples illustrate some of the variations.

◆ *Generate a single picking list based on starting the entire order quantity.* This represents the simplest scenario, where the picking list would be populated by all components with a flushing principle of Start.

◆ *Generate multiple picking lists based on different start quantities.* A typical scenario involves a production order quantity that represents multiple physical batches. You report a started quantity for each physical batch so that the picking list journal identifies component quantities for just one batch. Another scenario involves a production order quantity that represents a week's worth of production, but picking occurs in daily increments. You report a started quantity for each daily increment.

◆ *Generate multiple picking lists based on different operation numbers.* A typical scenario involves a production order with multiple operations and differing component requirements at each operation. For example, you can report the entire order quantity as started but segment the picking lists by operation. Another scenario involves an extended time between operations, so that you only report the started quantity for a specified operation.

◆ *Generate and immediately post a picking list based on the started quantity.* This approach is commonly termed forward flushing because the picking list is generated and then automatically posted. The approach reflects a policy in the Start dialogue.

◆ *Generate and immediately post a picking list based on the finished quantity.* A typical scenario would populate the picking list with components assigned a flushing principle of Finish. This approach is commonly termed back flushing because the picking list is automatically posted. The approach reflects the policies in the Report As Finished dialogue.

◆ *Manually generate a picking list.* This approach starts from the Picking List Journal where you specify the basis for automatically populating a picking list via a Create Lines dialogue. For example, you can automatically create lines based on a specified quantity or the order's started quantity. You post the picking list after reporting actual material usage. The approach ignores the flushing principle assigned to component items.

◆ *Generate a picking list when reporting labor.* You can optionally generate a picking list when reporting labor via route card journals or the MES capabilities.

◆ *Reverse the entries for a previously posted picking list.* When manually generating a picking list (described above), the basis for automatically populating the picking list can reflect reversing entries for a previously posted picking list. The resulting line items have a negative quantity, and line items can be deleted and modified. This approach is typically employed to record adjustments or corrections.

◆ *Issue unexpected components to an order.* This approach starts from the Picking List Journal where you manually add a line item for issuing the component. A manually-created line item represents an unexpected component which will be added to the Production BOM with a required quantity of zero. It will also result in a material substitution variance for a standard cost item. It does not represent an additional quantity for an existing component.

Report Production Order Picking via Auto-Deduction The concept of auto-deduction was mentioned in the previous point, but merits repeating. That is, you can generate and immediately post a picking list journal based on the started quantity (aka forward flushing) or the finished quantity (aka backward flushing).

7.7 Options for Labor Reporting

The internal operations within the routing for a started production order provide the basis for reporting actual operation time and unit completions, where the operation time can reflect labor and/or machine resources. Operation time and unit completions can be reported on a route card journal, and a route card journal is automatically generated when reporting labor via the MES capabilities. Labor can also be reported via auto-deduction. This section summarizes these major options for labor reporting.

Report Labor via Route Cards A route card journal is used to report operation time and unit completions by operation. [4] It consists of header information and one or more journal lines.

◆ *Report Operation Time by Operation.* Each journal line indicates the operation number, the resource and the actual hours expended. The route card journal provides several user options, such as overriding the basis for costing and indicating the employee performing the work. As part of a journal line, you can indicate the operation is completed so that remaining requirements are ignored.

---

[4] Labor can be reported via a route card journal or job card journal. The primary difference between the two involves the approach to time reporting. You specify the elapsed time on the route card, whereas you specify start and end times (with automatic calculation of the elapsed time) on the job card. In addition, the job card journal only applies when orders have been scheduled via the job scheduling method, which identifies a job for each time element such as setup and process time. This explanation focuses on using the route card journal for simplicity's sake.

◆ *Report Unit Completions by Operation.* Each journal line can also be used to report the units completed for an operation, and unit completions can be reported without a time entry. Unit completions are reported as a good quantity, with an optional incremental quantity for scrapped units and a reason code. Reporting unit completions for the last operation has special significance. The good unit completions can optionally update parent receipts by designating the report-as-finished flag. This represents one option for reporting a finished quantity, as described in a subsequent section (Section 7.8).

The unit completions and operation time provide measures of progress against the routing operation. The system automatically calculates a completion percentage based on actual versus expected process hours as one indicator of remaining work. The completion percentage can be manually overridden. The completion percentage for each operation can be used to schedule the remaining work for a production order.

The remaining time requirements for a routing operation can be ignored under several conditions: when the operation has been flagged as complete, when the entire routing has been flagged as complete; or when the order status becomes reported-as-finished.

Report Labor using the MES Capabilities The Manufacturing Execution System (MES) module supports data collection for reporting unit completions and operation time via clock-in and clock-out registrations for specific production orders and operations. Based on this registration information, the system automatically accumulates the times and unit completions by operation, which can then be used to create line items in route card (or job card) journals. This functionality builds on the time and attendance capabilities within the module, and also supports preparation of payroll data from a single source of labor data. The typical process to report labor for production orders using the MES approach is summarized in Figure 7.6 and described below.

Figure 7.6 Labor Reporting using the MES Capabilities

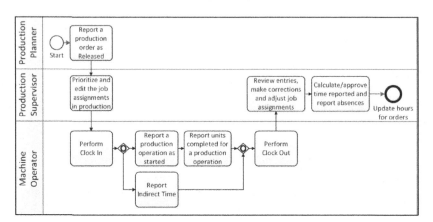

As the first step, the production planner indicates the production orders that are released or started, which triggers the generation of route cards that reflect routing operations. A started status represents an authorization to report actual production activities, and the step can also generate a picking list journal based on the Start dialogue policies.

◆ *Prioritize and Edit the Job Assignments in Production.* Prior to reporting production, the production supervisor uses a key form (termed the Edit Job List) to fine-tune the daily schedule, such as re-sequencing or moving jobs, assigning available resources, and designating high priority jobs. This form provides information about each production order, the material availability, and capacity loads to support decision making about efficiency and on-time completions. The resulting job list provides the machine operators the sequence to perform their daily tasks.

◆ *Perform Clock In and Clock Out, and Report Actual Production.* When reporting production, a machine operator or production worker can "clock in" to a resource group or a specific resource. The operator is presented up-to-date job information and related documents such as drawings and process specifications. The operator can start a specific job or start a bundle of multiple jobs, or indicate indirect time such as meetings. The operator provides feedback about units completed (including the scrap quantity) and updates the status of the operation, such as completed or stopped. The operator can "clock out" when done working at a resource, or done for the day.

◆ *Review Entries, Make Corrections and Adjust Job Assignments.* The production supervisor reviews and analyzes the reported time throughout the day, such as reviewing who has clocked in, correcting time entries, or shifting jobs to different machines or operators.

◆ *Calculate/Approve Time Reported.* At the end of the day, the supervisor performs a calculation to determine elapsed hours from the clock in/clock out transactions. The production supervisor may enter adjustments or identify absences, and then approve the information in order to update the hours reported for the production order. The approved information can also be transferred to a payroll or time-and-attendance system.

Report Labor using Auto-Deduction Operation time can be auto-deducted based on the started quantity or finished quantity. Auto-deduction involves several policies within the Route Group assigned to the operation, and several policies with the start dialogue (or report as finished dialogue) for updating order status.

7.8 Options for Reporting a Finished Quantity

The finished quantity of a production order can be reported in different ways. This section summarizes the three major options applicable to both the basic and advanced approach to warehouse management. A fourth option only applies to the advanced approach, where you report a finished quantity via a mobile device transaction. This section also summarizes the related approaches for updating order status to Reported as Finished, and the conditions which prevent a change to order status.

Option #1: Use the Report as Finished form The Report as Finished form can be accessed by starting from the Production Order form, or accessed directly, in order to report a finished quantity. Completing the transaction will automatically create and post an inventory journal for the finished quantity (labeled the Report as Finished Journal). The transaction can also change order status to *Reported as Finished* by selecting the End Job flag.

Option #2: Use the Report as Finished Journal The Report as Finished Journal form can be accessed by starting from the Production Order form, or accessed directly, in order to manually create a new journal for reporting a finished quantity. The journal consists of header information (identifying the production order) and one or more line items, where each line identifies an item and its finished quantity. The transaction can also change order status to *Reported as Finished* by selecting the Report as Finished flag for a journal line.

Option #3: Use the Route Card Journal for Reporting Unit Completions at the Last Operation When using routing information, the Route Card Journal (or Job Card Journal) can be accessed by starting from the Production Order form, or accessed directly, in order to report unit completions and operation time. When reporting for the last operation in the Production route, the good quantity can update the finished quantity by selecting the Production Report as Finished flag for a journal line. The transaction can change order status to *Reported as Finished* by also selecting the Operation Complete flag.

Update the Order Status to Reported as Finished As described above, the three options for reporting a finished quantity can update order status to *Reported as Finished.* You can also report a zero quantity in order to update the order status. However, several conditions can prevent a change to the order status, and a warning message identifies the conditions. You can override these warnings by using the Accept Errors flag when reporting the finished quantity. As one examples of missing feedback, each component must be completely issued, or flagged as completed in the picking list journal. As another example, each operation must be flagged as completed.

Report a Trashed Quantity for a Production Order Some scenarios will identify scrap when reporting a finished quantity rather than receiving the inventory for subsequent reporting of scrap. This scrapped quantity is also termed the error quantity or trashed quantity. The trashed quantity represents an incremental output in addition to good quantity. The trashed quantity is not tracked in inventory and does not result in an inventory transaction. The value of the trashed quantity can be charged to a specific G/L account but only for actual cost items, and it is identified as a substitution variance for standard cost items.

AX Terminology related to Reported as Finished The AX terminology about reporting a finished quantity can become confusing because the term "Report as Finished" has multiple contexts. The primary context involves the production order status of *Reported as Finished*, which means all production activities have been reported. You can report a finished quantity using several different approaches, as described above. This includes the Report as Finished form and the Report as Finished Journal, where indicating the "report as finished flag" can also update order status. In addition, you can use the route card journal for reporting a good quantity at the last operation, and indicating the "production report as finished flag" will update the finished quantity.

7.9 Costing for a Production Order

The estimated costs for a production order can be initially calculated by performing the Estimate task, where the calculated costs reflect the order quantity and the order-dependent BOM and routing. The Estimate task may be used to recalculate estimated costs after changes, such as changes to components or operations, or changes to the active cost records for items, labor rates, or overhead formulas.

The actual costs (termed realized costs) for a production order are automatically calculated based on reported production activities, such as actual material usage and operation times. You can view detailed transactions about reported activities on the Production Posting inquiry for a production order. Several reports summarize the activities for all current orders, including the raw materials in process report, the work in process report (for routing transactions), and the indirect costs in process report (for overheads incurred). You can analyze estimated and actual costs using the price calculation inquiry for the order. Cost information is shown for each component, operation, and applicable overhead formula.

Updating an Item's Actual Cost Actual costs are calculated after ending a production order for an actual cost item.

Calculated Variances for a Standard Cost Item Variances are calculated after ending a production order for a standard cost item. The variances reflect a comparison between the reported production activities and the item's standard cost calculation. [5] Four types of variances are calculated: lot size variance, production quantity variance, production price variance, and production substitution variance. Figure 7.7 identifies these four variances for a manufactured item. The figure also identifies similar variances related to co/by-products of a batch order. The common sources of order variances are shown in the bottom half of Figure 7.7, such as a different quantity issued or received.

You can analyze the order variances for a selected production order. The variances can also be viewed on the Variance Analysis Statement report and the Cost Estimating and Costing report. The Standard Cost Transactions inquiry provides another approach to analyzing order variances. For example, you can identify the variances associated with every production order for an item. In

---

[5] The calculated standard cost for a manufactured item reflects the specified BOM version, route version, quantity, calculation date, and active cost records as of the calculation date. Calculation of a manufactured item's cost was previously explained in Chapter 7.

order to anticipate variances prior to ending a production order, you can analyze the realized costs for a selected order or by using the Cost Estimates and Costing report.

Figure 7.7 Order Variances for Production Orders

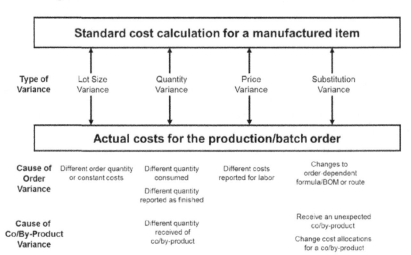

7.10 Coordinate Production Activities

A firm's S&OP game plans provide the primary driver of production activities. The key tools for coordinating these activities include planned production orders and action messages, which reflect the model of SCM decision-making embedded in coverage planning data for manufactured items (Section 2.3). The next section covers additional coordination tools when using routing data, such as production schedules and capacity analysis.

Planned Production Orders   The planned orders can be viewed on the Planned Production Orders form or the Planned Orders form, where the displayed information typically represents the current master plan.[6] Planned orders can be viewed based on selection criteria such as the buyer group and order date, so that the responsible planner can mark and firm the planned orders accordingly.

Actual production orders can be created from planned orders via a function termed *firming planned orders*.   You typically mark (via a check box) the planned orders needing to be firmed.   The generated orders have an assigned

---

[6] You can view information based on a selected set of master plan data or forecast plan data. For simplicity's sake the explanation focuses on the set of data representing the current master plan.

order status based on an item-related policy (embedded in the Coverage Group assigned to the item). A status of scheduled is a typical policy Execution of the firming function automatically deletes the selected planned orders, and creates a log for tracking which planned orders have been firmed and by whom.

The Planned Orders form can also be accessed in the context of making sales order delivery promises by using a Net Change Explosion, since this approach also creates planned orders.

In many cases, you may need to analyze the rationale for a planned production order prior to firming. You can view the net requirements and related action messages for a selected planned order. You can also view requirements associated with components and routing operations. The analysis may lead to one or more of the following actions prior to firming.

◆ Approve a planned order. Approving a planned production order will lock the scheduled date and quantity, and prevent it from being deleted by master scheduling logic or the Delete Plan task. In addition, it will also lock the BOM and routing information, so that planned changes will not be recognized.

◆ Change quantity and/or delivery date for the planned order.

◆ Re-schedule the planned order using a specified scheduling method and scheduling direction, with optional consideration of finite material and capacity.

◆ Split the planned order using a specified quantity and date.

◆ Group together several selected planned orders for the same item, with a total quantity for a single production order. The delivery date reflects the currently selected planned order.

◆ Identify a different source of supply (such as a purchase or transfer) by changing the planned production order to a planned purchase order or transfer order.

Some scenarios have correctly modeled their SCM decision making for selected items so that the planned production orders can be automatically firmed (within the time period defined by a firming fence). Other scenarios employ the freeze time fence to support near-term schedule stability in production, since master scheduling logic will place planned orders at the end of the frozen period. These time fence policies are embedded in the coverage group assigned to an item.

Action Messages   Action messages represent one of the key tools for coordinating production activities to meet the S&OP game plans. Master scheduling logic can generate action messages for planned and actual production orders. The logic reflects the action message policies embedded within the coverage group assigned to an item. The action messages can be viewed and acted upon in several different ways:

♦ View action messages for a selected item as part of the Net Requirements inquiry.

♦ View action messages for all items on the Actions form, and optionally apply the suggested action for a selected message or access the Action Graph.

♦ View related action messages (for a selected message) by accessing the Action Graph, and optionally apply a suggested action.

As a general guideline, you should view related action messages using the Action Graph in order to understand the context of other orders.

Messages about Calculated Delays   This message indicates that a production order delivery date will cause a delay in meeting a requirement date, and the production order typically has an associated "advance" action message. The messages can viewed from several different starting points (such as the Net Requirements inquiry), and you access the referenced order to indicate a change.

7.11 Production Schedules and Capacity Analysis

When using routing data, master scheduling logic can calculate capacity requirements and generate suggested production schedules for each resource. The visibility of these calculations is constrained by a capacity time fence expressed in days, which is normally defined as part of the policies assigned to a master plan. For example, the capacity time fence may reflect several weeks for near-term scheduling purposes in the current master plan, or it may reflect one year or longer for long-term capacity analysis in a set of master plan data for long range planning purposes.

Capacity Analysis   Capacity analysis reflects a comparison between a resource's available capacity and the requirements stemming from production orders. The nature of capacity analysis depends on the consideration of finite capacity limits, the set of master plan data, and the definition of resource requirements in routing operations.

♦ *Consideration of finite capacity.* A resource's available capacity can be viewed as infinite or finite. An infinite capacity viewpoint means that scheduling of each operation's duration considers the available working hours at a resource, but an unlimited number of orders can be scheduled concurrently. This means capacity analysis can identify overloaded periods.

A finite capacity viewpoint typically means that only one order can be scheduled concurrently during working hours, and that scheduling logic considers existing loads. Scheduling logic only considers a finite capacity limit for resources designated as having finite capacity.

◆ *Set of Master Plan data.* Capacity analysis can be viewed for a specified set of master plan data or forecast plan data. Several policies for a set of master plan determine whether finite capacity applies to planned production orders and the applicable time horizon (aka the finite capacity time fence).

◆ *Definition of an operation's resource requirements.* The resource requirements for an operation can be defined in several ways. For example, they may be specified for a single resource, a resource group, or a resource capability, and an operation may have requirements for a primary resource and secondary resources.

With these factors in mind, capacity analysis can be viewed for a resource (or a resource group) using a tabular or graphic format.

◆ *Tabular Format for Capacity Analysis.* The Capacity Load Inquiry provides a tabular format for load analysis of one resource or a resource group. It displays total load hours in daily increments and highlights overloaded days. You can view detailed reference information about routing operations comprising a daily load. A separate form (termed Capacity Reservations) provides a tabular format about all routing operations for the resource.

◆ *Graphical Format for Capacity Analysis.* The Capacity Load Graphical Inquiry provides a setup dialogue that determines how to display the information. For example, the information can be displayed in hours or percentages, and in specified increments (such as daily, weekly or monthly) for a specified range of dates. These time increments represent the continuum of detailed to aggregate capacity analysis, and the percentage viewpoint can highlight overloaded periods.

Additional variations include displaying loads for a range of resources, either as multiple graphics or as a single graphic with an accumulated load. Selected sources of loads can be excluded, such as loads stemming from planned orders. You cannot access detailed reference information about the operations comprising a resource load.

Production Schedules The nature of a production schedule depends on the three major factors mentioned above -- the definition of an operation's resource requirements, the consideration of capacity limits, and the set of master plan data.

A production schedule identifies each routing operation performed in the resource. It consists of the same detailed reference information as the load analysis drill-down, but is presented in a format more appropriate for communicating the needed action. In particular, it provides visibility of production orders at various order statuses so that production personnel can finish those already started as well as anticipate those that need to be started.

Production schedules can be displayed in different formats, such as tabular or Gantt chart. Each firm tends to customize their production schedule to fit their operations, but a typical tabular format can be described. A production schedule in tabular format identifies operations in a priority sequence with the highest priority operations listed first. The simplest sequencing rule is based on operation start (or ending) date and time. Operation information includes the remaining units and time and also the units completed to-date. It may include other information that proves useful to the planner or production personnel, such as the prior and next operation, the expected operation scrap percentage, and the operation description. Much of the information may be identified by the shop paperwork for each order, thereby minimizing the need for including it in the production schedule. The Operations List Inquiry provides one example of a production schedule.

Basic Sequencing Capabilities for a Production Schedule Some basic capabilities can be used to sequence the operations for a selected resource by accessing the Dispatching form. For example, you can view the current sequence of selected operations for the next day or two, manually change the sequence, and then perform scheduling to re-schedule the operations based on their assigned sequence.

An alternative approach to basic sequencing is included in the MES capabilities described earlier (Section 7.7). You can use the Edit Job List form to adjust the daily schedules, such as re-sequencing or moving jobs, assigning available resources, and designating high priority jobs. This form provides information about each production order, the material availability, and capacity loads to support decision making about efficiency and on-time completions. The resulting job list provides the machine operators the sequence to perform their daily tasks.

7.12 Performance Metrics for Production

Production performance can be assessed by several different metrics. One metric involves a comparison of actual costs against planned costs for production orders. Another metric involves on-time completion. One or more metrics of quality can also be used, such as failed test results on quality orders, production-related cases about quality, or production orders with a trashed quantity.

Review Actual vs Planned Costs for a Production Order The production supervisor can review the actual versus planned costs for a production order, either during or after execution of the production activities.

Review Actual vs Standard costs for a Production Order For a standard cost item, the production supervisor can review the actual versus standard costs for a production order, either during or after execution of the production activities. The production variances are only calculated after reporting the production order as Ended.

Review On-Time Completion of Production Orders The production supervisor can compare the actual reported-as-finished date of a production order against the scheduled completion date.

Review Failed Quality Orders related to Production When using quality orders, the quality manager can review the production-related quality orders that have failed the validation of test results. The quality orders and related test results can be reported during production operations or after reporting the finished quantity.

Review Production-Related Cases When using cases, the quality manager can review the production-related cases for production orders.

Review Production Orders with a Trashed Quantity The quality manager can review production orders with a trashed quantity (aka error quantity) and the associated reason codes.

7.13 Workspaces Related to Production Orders

Several predefined workspaces are related to production orders, as described in the following summary of each workspace and its applicable functionality.

Production Floor Management Workspace   This workspace primarily supports the production supervisor role.   It summarizes several aspects of information about production orders and their related operations (as of a selected date).   For example, it identifies the production orders to release and the component availability for each order, and it supports the release of selected orders.   It helps prioritize the sequence of jobs for released orders.   It identifies the jobs that need to be completed and the jobs with reported deviations (such as a scrap quantity).   In addition, it summarizes the number of jobs that are not yet started, stopped, and in progress.   By configuring the workspace, you can filter the displayed information for a selected resource, resource group and/or production unit.

The links provide access to information about production orders, resources, and the various production journals (such as the picking list journal or job card journal).   They also provide access to the calculation and approval of time and attendance information reported through the MES capabilities.   The labor reporting aspects of these MES capabilities also provide the basis for viewing staff attendance.

Cost Administration Workspace   This workspace identifies production orders with high variances, and the links provide access to reports/inquiries about production variances and postings.   Menu items provide access to production orders and batch orders.

Master Planning Workspace   This workspace identifies planned production orders, and also the action messages and calculated delay messages about production orders.

7.14 Additional Case Studies

Case 7.1: Production Worker Reporting via the Job Card Device Page   The Job Card Device page provides an alternative reporting approach for production workers when using the MES capabilities within the new Dynamics AX.   It works on mobile devices (such as tablets and phones) and supports touch-enabled reporting.   For example, the production worker can report the start (and started quantity) of a production order as well as the finished quantity, identify the operation being worked on, and view attachments about the operation.

Case 7.2: Advanced Planning and Scheduling (APS) Integration   A fabricated products company required APS capabilities to minimize setups and avoid additional equipment purchases for its line of extruded plastic products.   Multiple extrusion machines produced plastic pipes of varying diameters and colors.   Scheduling considerations included sequence-dependent setup time (based on pipe diameter and color), and machine capabilities for handling different products. Scheduling considerations also included machine-specific run rates, and secondary resources for tooling and skilled operators. To integrate an APS application, additional attributes were required for resources (e.g., machine capabilities), routing operations (e.g., setup attributes) and calendars (e.g. available crew size by shift).[7]

Case 7.3: Graphical Schedule Board for Production Orders   The production planners at a manufacturing company employed a graphical schedule board to coordinate production orders by viewing the related routing operations at selected work centers, and adjusting them accordingly.[8]   The graphical display could include both actual and planned production orders, and it reflected current information within AX as well as the standard scheduling logic.   It did not involve additional APS functionality.   Changing the displayed information via drag-and-drop techniques -- such as changing an operation duration, or assigning the operation to a different work center -- automatically updated the current information within AX.   Alternatively, the information could be adjusted in simulation mode to achieve the desired schedule, and then used to update the current information.   Using the graphical schedule board, the planners could perform every function related to a production order, such as firming a planned order, scheduling/releasing/starting an order, or viewing the BOM and route information.

7.15 Executive Summary

Production represents the distinctive competency of many manufacturers. Production activities can be coordinated and reported using production orders, and the significance of a single order affects these activities.   Several considerations apply to production orders, such as the order status within the order life cycle, the order-dependent BOM and routing, and the production order lead time.   Production activities can be reported against started orders, such as picking material, reporting operation time, and receiving finished quantities. Coordination of production activities is based on suggestions for planned orders, action messages and production schedules by resource.   The chapter reviewed several variations of production order processing, such as production inspection and the use of rework orders.

---

[7] See www.Preactor.com for additional information about their Advanced Scheduler module.
[8] See www.DynamicsSoftware.com for additional information about their Graphical Schedule Board.

Chapter 8

Basic Warehouse Management for Production Orders

The basic approach to warehouse management – also termed the Basic Inventory approach -- supports several variations in picking and receiving material for production orders. A simple production scenario provides the context for explaining the basic processes for picking and receiving. These two basic processes provide a baseline to explain the related life cycles, reversing transactions, and major variations. The two topics of picking and receiving are reflected in the following two groups of sections within the chapter.

1. Scenario #1 for Internal Production
2. Basic Process for Production Order Picking
3. Additional Steps in the Basic Process
4. Life Cycles Related to Production Order Picking
5. Reversing Transactions in Production Order Picking
6. Major Variations of Production Order Picking
7. Basic Process for Production Order Receiving
8. Life Cycles Related to Production Order Receiving
9. Reversing Transactions in Production Order Receiving
10. Major Variations of Production Order Receiving

Effective production scheduling represents a critical consideration for production order picking and receiving. A production schedule should reflect up-to-date S&OP game plans, capacity and material constraints, near term stability, and other factors such as production sequencing and a manageable level of expediting. These considerations will make life easier for warehouse management.

8.1 Scenario #1 for Internal Production

A simple production scenario provides a baseline for explaining the basic business processes related to production order picking and receiving. The simple scenario represents one of many variations in production, and there are several viewpoints of this scenario. From an engineering viewpoint, the scenario consists of a single-level bill of material (BOM) to produce an end-item from raw material components and a single operation within the routing. The warehouse is responsible for reporting picked material from raw material locations, and production is responsible for producing the end-item and reporting any adjustments to actual material usage. Work in process will be updated by the picked material and adjustments, and by reporting finished quantities. A finished quantity can be reported by production or warehouse workers. Figure 8.1 summarizes these engineering, production reporting, and warehouse management viewpoints. Arrows identify the various transactions.

The figure identifies the single-level bill of material and routing for the simple scenario where End-Item #1 is produced from Raw Material A (and other components) by a routing operation at Work Center #1 (aka a resource). A resource group identifies several similar work centers; the resource group has a common production input location (located at the start of production) and a common output location (located at the end of production). These are commonly termed floorstock or lineside locations and reflect the lean principle of stocking at the point of use.

Figure 8.1 Production Scenario #1 for Internal Manufacturing

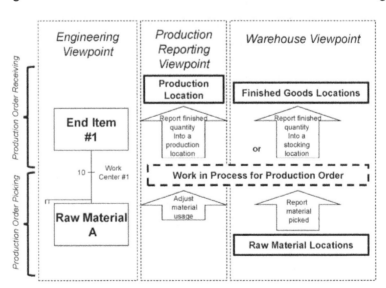

The arrows indicate key transactions for production and warehouse reporting. The figure indicates the different alternatives for reporting the finished quantity into a stocking location or a production location. The figure also identifies the relevant warehouse locations for raw material and finished goods as well as the work in process for the production order.

8.2 Basic Process for Production Order Picking

The previously-described production scenario provides the context of a basic process for production order picking. The basic process shown in Figure 8.2 consists of several steps typically performed by a machine operator and warehouse worker; however, there are many variations about the role responsibilities and steps. The figure also identifies the automatic step for generating the picking list journal. The process starts with the need to issue goods to production and ends with completed issues. This section provides an overview of the basic process and describes each step in more detail.

Figure 8.2 Basic Process for Production Order Picking

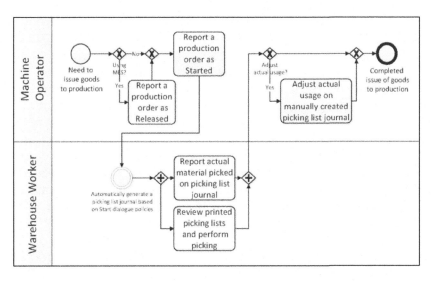

Overview The machine operator reports a production order as Started which acts as the trigger for creating a picking list journal (based on the Start dialogue policies). The operator may release the production order beforehand when using the Manufacturing Execution System (MES) functionality which generates route cards (that reflect routing information) so that a production supervisor can manually edit the production schedules.

The warehouse worker reviews the printed version of the picking list journal and reports actual material picked. The picked material is charged to work in process for the production order and deducted from inventory. It is typically delivered physically to production but not to a specific location.

In some cases, the machine operator may need to revise actual usage relative to the picked material. The machine operator manually creates a picking list journal containing the adjustments and then posts it.

Report a Production Order as Released The machine operator optionally reports a production order as Released, which can generate production paperwork (such as route cards) and also support MES functionality about detailed scheduling prior to reporting the order as Started.

Report a Production Order as Started The machine operator reports a production order as Started, which automatically generates a picking list journal based on the Start dialogue policies. As part of the Start dialogue, for example, the machine operator will start the entire order quantity and generate the picking list journal for components with a flushing principle of *Start*.

Report Actual Material Picked on the Picking List Journal The warehouse worker reports actual material picked by entering the data on the picking list journal and then physically delivering the components to production.

Review Printed Picking Lists The warehouse worker reviews the printed version of the picking list journal as a guide for performing activities. The printed document indicates the reserved quantity and location for each component, and provides bar-coded information to simplify data collection.

Adjust Actual Usage on a Manually-Created Picking List Journal In some cases, the machine operator may need to adjust actual usage relative to the picked material. The machine operator manually creates a picking list journal to identify the adjustments and then posts it.

Enforce the Sequence of Major Steps in the Basic Process Some scenarios need to limit the ability to change production order status, such as preventing a jump to a Started status so that orders must be reported as scheduled before they can be started. These companywide policies (defined on the Production Control Parameters form) consist of a matrix about the allowed changes from one status to another.

8.3 Additional Steps in the Basic Process

The basic process often includes several additional steps not shown in Figure 8.2 so that the diagram does not become too complex. Several examples were previously described as key considerations for a production order (Section 7.4), such as assigning a stop flag and identifying material shortages. Other examples are listed below.

Indicate Completion of Picking Activity   The remaining component requirements are ignored when (1) a specific component has been flagged as completely picked, (2) when a picking list journal has been flagged as complete, (3) when an operation linked to the material has been flagged as complete, or (4) when the production order status has been updated to reported as finished.

Indicate Component Scrap When Reporting Actual Material Usage
You can report component scrap for a line item on the picking list journal, where you identify a separate scrap quantity and an optional reason code.

Move Unused Raw Material Back to Stocking Location   In some scenarios, actual material usage is less than the picked quantity for a component; the unused inventory needs to be returned to a stocking location. It is first necessary to reverse the picked quantity (out of work in process) via a manually-created picking list journal. You can indicate the stocking location on the journal line before posting the journal.

8.4 Life Cycles Related to Production Order Picking

The basic process involves several related constructs where the status for each construct reflects various steps in the process. Figure 8.3 summarizes this information for the basic process. The steps represent the essential touch points for updating status. Shading highlights the key steps and constructs related to the Basic Inventory approach, which includes use of the picking list journal.

Reporting a production order as Started provides the starting point of the process, since this will automatically generate the picking list journal based on the Start dialogue policies. In many scenarios, starting the order also reserves component inventory (based on the reservation policy for the order). The component's inventory status changes to *deducted* after reporting actual material picked and posting the picking list journal. The inventory status of a component and the parent item are shown on the right side of the figure. Their status will also be updated by reporting a finished quantity and by ending an order.

Figure 8.3   Life Cycles Related to the Basic Process
for Production Order Picking

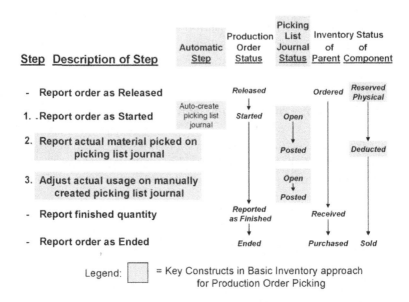

Legend: = Key Constructs in Basic Inventory approach
for Production Order Picking

8.5 Reversing Transactions in Production Order Picking

The ability to reverse transactions requires an understanding of the current point within the business process and the associated status of key constructs. Borrowing from the previous figure, Figure 8.4 illustrates the steps within the basic process (shown in grey text) and the various points at which you can perform reversing transactions (shown in black text). The figure also illustrates the impact of a reversing transaction on status, and the arrow indicates the resulting point in the business process. As identified by step numbers in the figure, you can reverse transactions (3X) after reporting actual material usage on the picking list journal and (AnyX) at any time prior to ending the production order.

Step 3X: Create a Picking List Journal with Reversing Entries   You can reverse one or more transactions from a previously posted picking list. As the starting point, you manually generate a picking list journal with lines created from a previously-posted picking list. The lines (with a negative quantity) can be adjusted prior to posting the picking list. For example, some of the transactions can be deleted (because they do not need to be reversed) or the negative quantity can be reduced to indicate a partial reversal.

Figure 8.4   Reversing Transactions in the Basic Process
for Production Order Picking

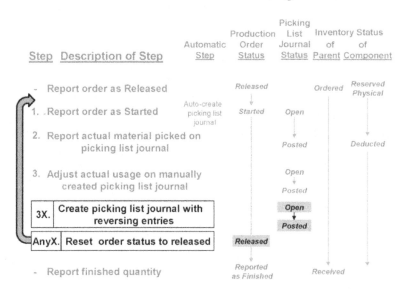

Step AnyX: Reset Order Status for a Production Order A production order can be reset to a previous status at any time prior to the *Ended* status. You indicate the desired order status on the reset order dialogue. For example, as shown in the figure, order status may be changed to *Released* from *Started* so that all transactions about actual production activities will be reversed.

8.6 Major Variations of Production Order Picking

The basic process for production order picking provides the baseline for explaining key considerations and major variations. Many of these were covered in the previous chapter (Sections 7.5 and 7.6), such as the significance of a single order and picking list journal, the warehouse source of components, the variations in generating and posting a picking list journal, and auto-deduction. Two additional variations involve serialized and batch-controlled material.

Picking Batch-Controlled Items The batch number(s) can be identified when reporting actual picking against the picking list journal. When using reservations, the reserved batch number(s) will be identified on the picking list journal.

Picking Serialized Items The serial number(s) can be identified when reporting actual picking against the picking list journal.

8.7 Basic Process for Production Order Receiving

The production scenario #1 provides a context for explaining a basic business for production order receiving. The basic process shown in Figure 8.5 consists of several steps typically performed by a machine operator and warehouse worker, but there are many variations about the role responsibilities and reporting approaches. The process starts with the need to receive a finished quantity and ends with a completed receipt. This section provides an overview of the basic process and describes each step in more detail.

Figure 8.5   Basic Process for Production Order Receiving

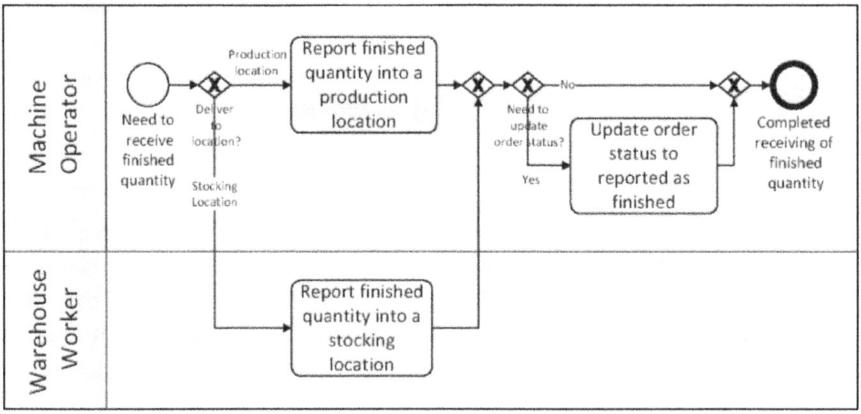

Overview   The finished quantity of a production order can be reported by different roles using different approaches and delivered to different locations. As illustrated in the figure, a finished quantity may be reported into a production location by the machine operator, or it may be reported into a stocking location by a warehouse worker. The finished quantity may be reported multiple times for a given order, or reported once when it represents the entire order quantity. The machine operator updates the order status to *Reported as Finished* after all production output has been reported.

Report the Finished Quantity into a Production Location   The machine operator can report the finished quantity into a production location. The finished quantity can be reported for the entire order quantity, or it may be reported for multiple receipts. Reporting a finished quantity that represents the last of the production output can be flagged, so that the order status will be updated to *reported as finished.*

Report the Finished Quantity into a Stocking Location The warehouse worker can report the finished quantity into a stocking location. The finished quantity can be reported for the entire order quantity, or it may be reported for multiple receipts. Reporting a finished quantity that represents the last of the production output can be flagged, so that the order status will be updated to *reported as finished.*

Update Order Status to Reported as Finished When reporting finished quantities, the last of the production output can be flagged so that the order status will be updated to *Reported as Finished.* If needed, you can report a zero quantity in order to update the order status. An order status of *Reported as Finished* means that any remaining requirements for material or capacity will be ignored, and any difference between the ordered quantity and received quantity will also be ignored.

8.8 Life Cycles Related to Production Order Receiving

The basic process involves several related constructs, where the status for each construct reflects various steps in the process. Figure 8.6 summarizes this information for the basic process, and only displays those steps representing the essential touch points for updating status. The major constructs include the production order and an inventory journal for each finished quantity (termed the Report as Finished Journal).

Figure 8.6 Life Cycles Related to the Basic Process
for Production Order Receiving

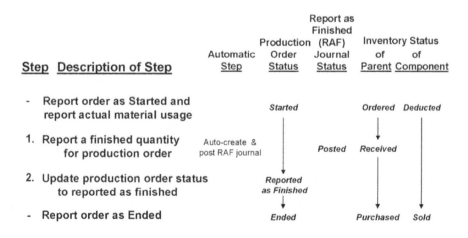

Reporting a finished quantity provides the starting point of the process, and it automatically creates and posts an inventory journal for the finished quantity. There are several option for reporting a finished quantity, as described in the previous chapter (Section 7.8). A separate step for updating order status only applies when it has not already been updated by reporting the last of the finished quantities. The right side of the figure illustrates the inventory status associated with the parent item and a component for the production order.

8.9 Reversing Transactions in the Basic Process

The ability to reverse transactions requires an understanding of the current point within the business process, and the associated status of key constructs. Borrowing from the previous figure, Figure 8.7 illustrates the steps within the basic process (shown in grey text) and the various points at which you can perform reversing transactions (shown in black text). As identified by step numbers in the figure, you can reverse transactions (1X) after reporting a finished quantity and (2) after updating order status to *Reported as Finished.*

Figure 8.7 Reversing Transactions in the Basic Process for Production Order Receiving

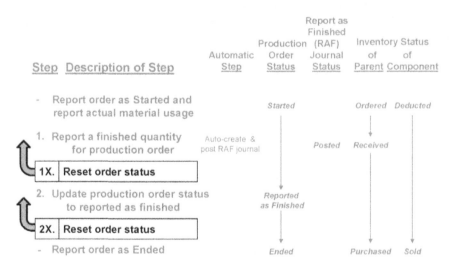

Step 1X: Reset Order Status for a Production Order You can reset the order status from Started to Released (or earlier) in order to back out all transactions for finished quantities and picking transactions.

Step 2X: Reset Order Status for a Production Order   Resetting the order status from Started to Released (or earlier) will back out all transactions for finished quantities and picking transactions. Resetting to a Started status has no impact.

8.10 Major Variations of Production Order Receiving

The basic process for production order receiving provides the baseline for explaining key considerations and major variations. Many of these were covered in the previous chapter (Sections 7.5 and 7.6), such as the significance of a single order, the options for reporting a finished quantity, and production inspection. Two additional variations involve serialized and batch-controlled material.

Receive Batch-Controlled Items   A batch-controlled item involves assignment of the batch number(s) when reporting a finished quantity. It may also involve reporting of a batch disposition code.

Receive Serialized Items   A serialized item involves the assignment of serial numbers when reporting a finished a finished quantity.

8.11 Additional Case Studies

Case 8.1: Preferred Equipment and the Warehouse Source of Components   A manufacturing company used routing information to indicate the preferred equipment for producing an item.   For example, the resource requirements for a routing operation can identify a dedicated machine (specified as the required resource for the operation), or as any machine within an interchangeable group of machines (specified as the required resource group for the operation). Other routing operations indicated a preferred machine based on the required capability or a minimum capability, or the production quantity (specified as a different route version with a quantity breakpoint).   The scheduling logic would suggest the preferred machine, and the assigned resource determined which warehouse location should supply the components.

Case 8.2: Correcting Errors About the Picked Components   The warehouse workers at a manufacturing company sometimes made a mistake in reporting the quantity picked for a production order or they needed to completely reverse an entire picking list. In these cases, they manually generated a picking list journal with lines created from the previously posted picking list. The lines (with a negative quantity) were adjusted prior to posting the picking list. For example, some of the lines were deleted (because they did not need to be reversed) or the negative quantity was reduced to indicate a partial reversal or correction.

8.12 Executive Summary

The basic approach to warehouse management supports several variations in picking and receiving material for production orders. As a starting point, a simple production scenario for internal manufacturing provided the context for explaining the basic processes for picking and receiving. Given this context, the chapter described a based process for order-based picking, and for reporting finished quantities. For each process, the chapter explained the related life cycles, reversing transactions and major variations.

Several case studies illustrated the variations. These included preferred equipment and the warehouse source of components, and correcting errors about the picked components.

Chapter 9

Advanced Warehouse Management for Production Orders

The advanced approached to warehouse management – also termed the Advanced WMS approach -- supports multiple variations in picking and receiving material for production orders. A simple production scenario provides the context for explaining the basic processes for picking and receiving. These two basic processes provide a baseline to explain the related life cycles, reversing transactions, and major variations. The two topics of picking and receiving are reflected in the following two groups of sections within the chapter.

1. Scenario #2 for Internal Production
2. Basic Process for Production Order Picking
3. Additional Steps in the Basic Process
4. Life Cycles Related to Production Order Picking
5. Key Constructs for Production Order Picking
6. Reversing Transactions in Production Order Picking
7. Major Variations of Production Order Picking
8. Basic Process for Production Order Receiving
9. Life Cycles Related to Production Order Receiving
10. Reversing Transactions in Production Order Receiving
11. Key Constructs for Production Order Receiving
12. Major Variations of Production Order Receiving
13. Alternatives for Reporting the Finished Quantity

Effective production scheduling represents a critical consideration for picking and receiving. The schedules should reflect up-to-date S&OP game plans, capacity and material constraints, near term stability, and other factors such as production sequencing and a manageable level of expediting. These considerations will make life easier for warehouse management.

9.1 Scenario #2 for Internal Manufacturing

A simple production scenario provides a baseline for explaining the Advanced WMS approach to production order picking and receiving. It can be called Production Scenario #2 to differentiate it from the simple Production Scenario #1 that was used for explaining the Basic Inventory approach (Section 8.1). The slight differences in Scenario #2 will be used to highlight the unique aspects of raw material picking work to a production input location, the use of a production output location, and the alternatives for reporting finished quantities via mobile device and client transactions.

There are several viewpoints of this simple production scenario. From an engineering viewpoint, the scenario consists of a single level bill of material (BOM) to produce an end-item from raw material components, and a single operation within the routing. From a production reporting viewpoint, the key constructs consist of a production order and picking list journal. The production order quantity represents a single production run with a single picking list journal in this simple scenario. Production is responsible for reporting actual component usage against the picking list journal, and oftentimes for reporting the finished quantity for the production order.

From a warehouse viewpoint, the key constructs consist of different warehouse locations for raw materials, production floorstock, and finished goods. The key transactions involve delivering raw materials to production input locations and putaway of finished goods to stocking locations. Oftentimes, warehouse workers are responsible for reporting the finished quantity, or for reporting the finished quantity as part of reporting putaway. Figure 9.1 summarizes these different viewpoints of engineering, production reporting and warehouse management, especially the responsibilities for reporting transactions.

The figure identifies the single-level bill of material and routing for the simple scenario, where End-Item #1 is produced from Raw Material A (and other components) by a routing operation at Work Center #1 (aka a resource). A resource group identifies several similar work centers, and the resource group has a common production input location (located at the start of production) and a common output location (located at the end of production). These are commonly termed floorstock or lineside locations, and reflect the lean principle of stocking at the point of use.

Figure 9.1   Production Scenario #2 for Internal Manufacturing

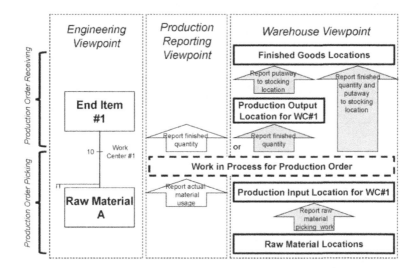

The arrows indicate key transactions for production reporting and warehouse reporting, and the figure identifies the mobile device transactions via grey shading. The figure indicates the different alternatives for reporting the finished quantity via screen or a mobile device, or as part of reporting putaway via a mobile device. The figure also identifies the relevant warehouse locations for raw material and finished goods, and the production input and output locations for the work center.

9.2 Basic Process for Production Order Picking

The previously-described production scenario provides the context of a basic process for production order picking, with a focus on order-based picking rather than wave picking. The basic process shown in Figure 9.2 consists of several steps typically performed by a machine operator and warehouse worker, but there are many variations about the role responsibilities. It highlights the mobile device transaction for raw material picking with grey shading, and identifies several automatic actions within the system. The process starts with the need to issue goods to production and ends with the completed issues to production.

Overview   The machine operator reports a production order as Released, which acts as the trigger for several automatic actions to support actual production. This includes creating and releasing a production wave for the order, which triggers creation of picking work for delivering components to a production input location when it has insufficient component inventory.

Figure 9.2   Basic Process for Production Order Picking

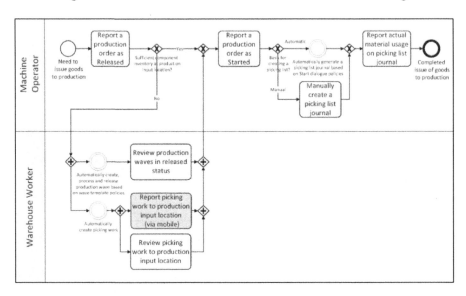

The warehouse worker reviews the released production waves and the associated picking work. Using the mobile device, the warehouse worker reports the picking work (consisting of picks and puts) for delivering components to the designated production input location.

When ready, the machine operator reports a production order as Started, which automatically generates a picking list journal (based on the Start dialogue policies). The machine operator reports actual material usage on the picking list journal. In some cases, the machine operator will manually generate a picking list as an alternative to automatic generation, or to identify unexpected component requirements. In either case, the machine operator posts the picking list journal after reporting actual material usage.

Report a Production Order as Released   The machine operator reports a production order as Released, which acts as the trigger for several automatic actions to support actual production. The release step automatically reserves the component inventory (based on the reservation policy for the production order). It will automatically create, process and release a production wave for the production order (based on policies within the applicable production wave template). The "process" step for a production wave can also trigger creation of raw material picking work for delivering components to a production input location.

Review Production Waves in Released Status   The warehouse worker reviews released production waves to identify which production orders require delivery of components to production input locations, and optionally prints a picking list for a production wave..

Report Picking Work to the Production Input Location (via Mobile Device)   Using the mobile device, the warehouse worker reports work for picking components from stocking locations and delivering them to production input locations.

Review Picking Work for Production Input Location   The warehouse worker can review and print the work order for delivering components to the production input location. The printed document provides bar-coded information to simplify recording of the work.

Report a Production Order as Started   The machine operator reports a production order as Started, which automatically generates a picking list journal based on the Start dialogue policies. As part of the Start dialogue, for example, the machine operator will start the entire order quantity and generate the picking list journal for components with a forward flushing principle.

Based on the reservation policy for the production order, the component inventory can be automatically reserved (at the time of releasing or starting the order), so that the printed picking list indicates the reserved quantity for each component.

Manually Create a Picking List Journal   In some cases, the machine operator will manually generate a picking list as an alternative to automatic generation, or to identify reversing transactions for previously reported material usage. It may serve other purposes, such as identifying unexpected requirements so that the warehouse worker can use the printed picking list to pick and deliver additional material.

Report Actual Material Usage on Picking List Journal   The machine operator reports actual material usage on the picking list journal. For a given component, the machine operator can indicate when material usage has been completely reported so that remaining requirements (if any) will be ignored. The machine operator posts the picking list journal when completed. .

9.3 Additional Steps in the Basic Process

The basic process often includes several additional steps or slight variations which are not shown in Figure 9.2 so that the diagram does not become too complex. Several examples were previously described as key considerations for a production order (Section 7.4), such as assigning a stop flag and identifying material shortages. Other examples are listed below.

Report a Production Order as Started Using the Mobile Device This transaction reflects the default values for start dialogue policies that have been defined for the user.

Report Component Scrap Using the Mobile Device Reporting component scrap via a mobile device transaction will automatically create and post a separate picking list journal for the specified production order, component item, quantity, and production input location.

Report Component Scrap When Reporting Actual Material Usage on the Picking List Journal You can report component scrap for a line item on the picking list journal, where you identify a separate scrap quantity and an optional reason code.

Report Actual Usage of Additional Components You can report usage of an additional component by adding it as a line item on the picking list journal.

Move Unused Raw Material Back to Stocking Location Using the Mobile Device In many scenarios, the unused inventory at the production input location needs to be returned to a stocking location. For example, the quantity for an entire license plate (such as an entire pallet or barrel) can be delivered to the input location by raw material picking work, so that you need to move the item's unused inventory back to stock. Some scenarios will leave the unused inventory at the production input location to support subsequent production orders, thereby reducing or eliminating creation of raw material picking work.

9.4 Life Cycles Related to Production Order Picking

The basic process involves several related constructs, where the status for each construct reflects various steps in the process. Figure 9.3 summarizes this information for the basic process, and only displays those steps representing the essential touch points for updating status. Grey shading highlights the key steps and constructs related to the Advanced WMS approach. These key constructs include the production wave and related raw material picking work, the production input locations, and the picking list journal.

Figure 9.3 Life Cycles Related to the Basic Process for Production Order Picking

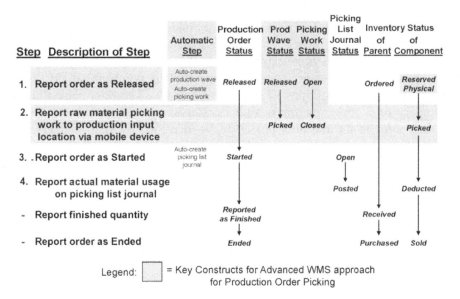

Step	Description of Step	Automatic Step	Production Order Status	Prod Wave Status	Picking Work Status	Picking List Journal Status	Inventory Status of Parent	Inventory Status of Component
1.	Report order as Released	Auto-create production wave Auto-create picking work	Released	Released	Open		Ordered	Reserved Physical
2.	Report raw material picking work to production input location via mobile device			Picked	Closed			Picked
3.	Report order as Started	Auto-create picking list journal	Started			Open		
4.	Report actual material usage on picking list journal					Posted		Deducted
-	Report finished quantity		Reported as Finished				Received	
-	Report order as Ended		Ended				Purchased	Sold

Legend: ☐ = Key Constructs for Advanced WMS approach for Production Order Picking

The release to warehouse step provides the starting point of the process, where you report a production order as released. For the basic process of order-based picking, this step will automatically create, process and release a production wave for the production order (based on wave template policies), and the released wave creates the picking work for delivering components to the production input location. The step also reserves component inventory (based on the reservation policy for the order).

As you report picking work, the component's inventory status changes to *picked* and the on-hand inquiries no longer display this inventory. The status of the production wave changes to *Picked* after reporting all related picking work. Reporting the production order as Started will automatically create the picking list journal, and reporting actual component usage (and posting the journal) changes the component's inventory status to *Deducted*. The inventory status of a component and the parent item are shown on the right side of Figure 9.3, and their status will be updated by the additional steps to report the finished quantity and end the production order.

Each of the major variations for production order picking and receiving has slightly different steps which involve differences in the life cycles and status for the key constructs. Subsequent sections describe the major variations and similar figures illustrate the related life cycles.

9.5 Reversing Transactions in the Basic Process

The ability to reverse transactions requires an understanding of the current point within the business process, and the associated status of key constructs. Borrowing from the previous figure, Figure 9.4 illustrates the steps within the basic process (shown in grey text) and the various points at which you can perform reversing transactions (shown in black text). The figure also illustrates the impact of a reversing transaction on status, and the arrows indicate the resulting point in the business process. As identified by step numbers in the figure, you can reverse transactions (1X) after initially creating the raw material picking work for a released production wave, (4X) after reporting actual material usage on the picking list journal, and (AnyX) at any time prior to ending the production order.

Figure 9.4   Reversing Transactions in the Basic Process
for Production Order Picking

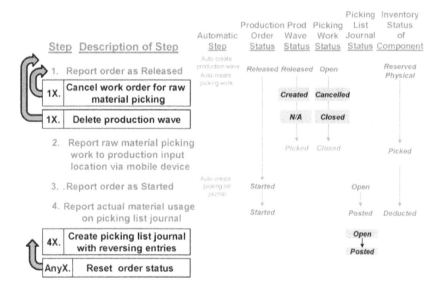

Step 1X: Cancel Work Order for Raw Material Picking You can cancel a Work Order prior to reporting any work, which changes the work order status to *Cancelled* and the wave status to *Created*. At this point, you can modify the production order (such as a changed quantity), and release the order again to create the picking work for the wave. Alternatively, you can manually process and release the wave again, which will also create the picking work. If applicable, you can even delete the order after resetting its order status to *Created*.

Step 1X: Delete the Production Wave After cancelling the related work orders, you can delete a production wave. The figure displays a status of "N/A" to indicate the deletion. At this point, releasing the order again will create another production wave and its associated work orders.

Step 3X: Delete the Picking List Journal for a Production Order You can delete a picking list journal prior to posting it. This step is not shown in the figure.

Step 4X: Create a Picking List Journal with Reversing Entries You can reverse one or more transactions from a previously posted picking list. As the starting point, you manually generate a picking list journal with lines created from a previously posted picking list. The lines (with a negative quantity) can be adjusted prior to posting the picking list. For example, some of the transactions can be deleted (because they do not need to be reversed) or the negative quantity can be reduced to indicate a partial reversal.

Step AnyX: Reset Order Status for a Production Order A production order can be reset to a previous status at any time prior to the *Ended* status. You indicate the desired order status on the reset order dialogue. For example, order status may be changed to *Created* to allow deletion, or changed to *Released* from *Started* so that the system automatically reverses all transactions about actual production activities.

9.6 Key Constructs for Production Order Picking

The Advanced WMS approach for issuing goods to production involves several key constructs in addition to the production order and its Production BOM/routing. These key constructs include reservations, production input locations, the production wave and related raw material picking work, and the picking list journal.

Reservation Policies for a Production Order The reservation policy assigned to a production order determines when components will be reserved relative to order status. In most scenarios, you select a reservation policy so that components will be automatically reserved at the time of releasing the production order. A related reservation policy determines whether components must be fully reserved or partially reserved when releasing a production order to the warehouse.

The reservation policy for an order is initially inherited as a companywide or site-specific policy and it can be overridden.   Some scenarios employ a reservation policy of Manual.   You can view and update reservations for components in the Production BOM or the Picking List Journal by accessing the Reservations form.

Production Input Locations A production input location is identified on raw material picking work as the "put" location. It is typically defined as a non-LP-controlled location to avoid additional details in reporting actual material usage. In addition, the production input location is normally assigned to raw material picking work based on the resource (or resource group) that needs the raw material.   However, some scenarios do not employ routings, so that the assignment can reflect a warehouse-specific default value.

The production input location can be defined for a resource group (such as a common location for multiple machines) and optionally overridden for a resource with the group (such as a machine-specific location). The automatic assignment of a production input location to raw material picking work reflects the resource or resource group performing a routing operation, which is determined by scheduling logic for production orders.

The linkage between a routing operation and its production input location involves several interrelated considerations.   First, the operation sequence number of the routing operation provides the basis for identifying required BOM components with the same operation number. Second, each BOM component must be defined with the relevant operation number and a "resource consumption" policy. The resource consumption policy ensures that component requirements will be linked to the assigned resource (or resource group), which ultimately provides the basis for assignment of an input location to raw material picking work. A previous chapter discussed the assignment of production input locations as one of the options for the warehouse source of components (Section 3.5).

Work Orders for Raw Material Picking and the Inventory at Production Input Locations   Several factors impact the creation of work orders for raw material picking and the related consideration about inventory at production input locations.

◆ *Insufficient Component Inventory at the Production Input Location.* Raw material picking work will only be created when the production input location has insufficient inventory to meet requirements.

◆ *Consideration of all Components in the Production BOM.* The creation of raw material picking work reflects all Production BOM components (regardless of flushing principle) at the time of creation.

◆ *Delivery of Entire Quantity for a License Plate (versus Exact Quantity).* When a raw material item is stocked in a location that is not license plate controlled, the raw material pick work will suggest the exact quantity to meet requirements. In contrast, the raw material picking work will suggest delivery of the entire quantity on a license plate when the material is stocked in a license plate controlled location, even though it is greater than the required quantity for a component. In addition, multiple occurrences of the same component in a BOM can result in raw material picking work for multiple license plates.

◆ *Visibility of Component Inventory at the Production input Location.* After reporting raw material picking, an inventory status of "picked" applies to the component. This means it is not visible in on-hand inquiries. However, inventory that represents an over-issued quantity remains visible in on-hand inquiries. As a result of under-reporting actual material usage and then reporting a production order as finished, the "picked" status no longer applies and the unused inventory becomes visible.

Significance of a Production Wave Template   The wave template determines whether wave planning steps will be performed manually or automatically after reporting a production order as released. For example, many wave planning scenarios will employ automatic assignment of components to an existing production wave, and manual steps to process and release the wave. A subsequent section provides further explanation about production wave planning as a major variation (Section 9.7).

Mobile Device Transactions   The primary mobile device transaction consists of raw material picking to a production input location. As part of defining the menu item, you select the policy for *use existing work* and the work order type for *raw material picking*. A work template and a location directive are also defined for the work order type of *raw material picking*. Once created, you can review this picking work by accessing it for the related production order (on the

Production Order form), for the related production wave (on the Production Wave form), or for a selected work order (on the All Work form).

Additional mobile device transactions include starting a production order, reporting component scrap, and moving unused material from the production input location to a stocking location.

Picking List Journals   The production order and its related picking list journal(s) represent critical tools for coordination and reporting of production and warehouse activities.   Their significance can differ widely depending on the scenario, as described in a previous chapter about considerations for production order picking (Section 7.6).   In a simple scenario, for example, the production order represents a single production run and the picking list journal contains all components and reflects the entire order quantity.

9.7 Major Variations of Production Order Picking

The basic process for production order picking provides the baseline for explaining key considerations and major variations.   Many of these were covered in a previous chapter (Sections 7.5 and 7.6), such as the significance of a single order and picking list journal, the warehouse source of components, the variations in generating and posting a picking list journal, and auto-deduction. Several additional variations involve a simple inventory transaction, serialized and batch-controlled material, and wave planning for production.

Simple Inventory Transaction for Production Order Picking   The use of raw material picking work is optional, so that you can simply report actual usage on the picking list journal.   This means that releasing a production order does not create raw material picking work.   It also means that the production input location for a resource group (or resource) should be blank, so that the reserved inventory reflects the stocking location of a component.   The simple inventory transaction of the picking list journal applies to both the basic and advanced approaches.

Picking Batch-Controlled Items   The picking work for batch-controlled items is impacted by reservation logic.   That is, the Reservation Hierarchy assigned to a component item determines whether its batch numbers will be reserved or not.   Reservations of specific batch numbers are critical in many scenarios, such as shelf-life items involving FEFO reservations.   As a result, the relevant batch will be displayed and printed on the work line for the work order, and also displayed on the mobile device when reporting the picking work.

Two additional policies about raw material picking work must be defined for correctly supporting reservations of batch-controlled items. These policies are defined as part of the Location Directive Actions related to the work order type for raw material picking, where you indicate the pick should be "Batch-Enabled" and also select the relevant "Strategy" for locating material. For example, the strategy should be "FEFO Batch Reservations" in order to correctly support picking of shelf-life items.

Other aspects of picking batch-controlled items can differ based on the use of license plates and the quantities involved. For example, the picking work may identify specific license plates (at an LP-controlled location), or the target license plate for picking work may contain multiple items and batch numbers. In addition, the picking work reflects the restricted usage policies for batch disposition codes that can be assigned to batch numbers.

Picking Serialized Items   The picking work for a serialized item is not typically impacted by reservation logic because of the item's Reservation Hierarchy, where serial numbers are below the location. The picking work can differ based on the use of license plates and the quantities involved. For example, the picking work may identify a specific license plate containing multiple serial numbers of an item, or the target license plate for picking work may contain multiple items and serial numbers.

Variations of Wave Picking for Production   A wave picking approach commonly refers to a grouping of released production orders with the same start date, so that a single wave contains the raw material picking work for multiple orders. The grouping is termed a production wave, or wave for short. There are many variations of a wave picking approach. At its simplest, a production wave reflects the raw material picking work for a single production order, so that the wave picking approach is frequently termed order-based picking. This variation was employed in the basic process for production order picking described earlier, where each wave was automatically created and released by reporting a production order as Released. Other variations involve wave picking for a grouping of production orders, which represents the more common reference for a wave picking approach. The planning aspects of wave picking for a group of released production orders consist of several steps typically performed by a warehouse planner. Some of the steps can be performed automatically to reflect the planner's normal decision making about wave planning, as modeled by policies within a wave template. For example, a production wave template might be defined so that releases of different production orders at different times will be automatically added to an existing wave.

9.8 Basic Process for Production Order Receiving

The production scenario #2 provides a context for explaining a basic business for production order receiving. The basic process shown in Figure 9.5 consists of several steps typically performed by a machine operator and warehouse worker, but there are many variations about the role responsibilities and reporting approaches. The business process starts with the need to receive a finished quantity and ends with completed receipts. The starting point shows three alternatives for reporting the finished quantity. The figure uses grey shading to highlight the mobile device transactions, and it identifies the automatic step for creating putaway work. This section provides an overview of the basic process and describes each step in more detail.

Figure 9.5 Basic Process for Production Order Receiving

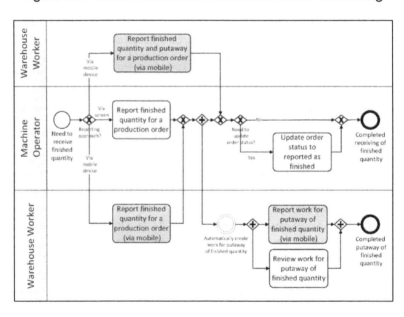

Overview   The finished quantity of a production order can be reported using several different approaches, and three approaches are illustrated in Figure 9.5. The finished quantity can be reported by the machine operator (using the client) in one approach, or it can be reported by the warehouse worker (using the mobile device) in another approach. In many cases, the finished quantity is placed in a production output location and a warehouse operator (using the mobile device) can report putaway work to a stocking location. Alternatively, the warehouse or production worker can report both finished quantity and putaway using a mobile device transaction. The finished quantity may be reported multiple times for a given order, or reported once when it represents the entire order quantity. The machine operator updates the order status to *Reported as Finished* after all production activities have been reported.

Report the Finished Quantity for a Production Order (via the Client)
The machine operator use the client to report the finished quantity into a production output location. The finished quantity can be reported for the entire order quantity, or it may be reported for multiple receipts. Each receipt triggers automatic creation of putaway work. Reporting a finished quantity that represents the last of the production output can be flagged, so that the order status will be updated to *Reported as Finished.*

When applicable, the machine operator reports the trashed quantity (aka error quantity) for a production order and an optional reason code. The trashed quantity is not tracked in inventory, and the value of the scrapped inventory is charged to an inventory loss account.

Report the Finished Quantity for a Production Order (via Mobile Device)
The warehouse worker uses the mobile device to report the finished quantity into a production output location. The finished quantity can be reported for the entire order quantity, or it may be reported for multiple receipts. Each receipt triggers automatic creation of putaway work. The system automatically prints a label as part of reporting the finished quantity so that the label can be attached to each license plate.

Report the Finished Quantity and Putaway for a Production Order (via Mobile Device)
The warehouse worker uses the mobile device to report both the finished quantity and putaway to a stocking location. The finished quantity can be reported for the entire order quantity, or it may be reported for multiple receipts. The system automatically prints a label as part of reporting the finished quantity so that the label can be attached to each license plate.

Update Order Status to Reported as Finished (via the Client)
When reporting finished quantities via the client, the last of the production output can be flagged so that the order status will be updated to *Reported as Finished.* However, when reporting via mobile devices, a separate "report as finished" transaction must be reported via the client. A zero quantity can be reported in order to update the order status. An order status of *Reported as Finished* means that any remaining requirements for material or capacity will be ignored, and any difference between the ordered quantity and received quantity will also be ignored.

Report Work for Putaway of Finished Quantity (via Mobile Device)
The warehouse worker uses the mobile device to report putaway work for a
finished quantity.

Review Work for Putaway of Finished Quantity   The warehouse worker
can review and print the work for putaway of the finished quantity.   The printed
document provides bar-coded information to simplify recording of the work.

Report the Last Pallet for a Production Order (via Mobile Device)   The
"last pallet" transaction represents an additional step not shown in Figure 9.5,
The need for reporting "last pallet" stems from the AX functionality related to
delivering inventory to production input locations via raw material picking work.
The required quantity of inventory has a status of *Picked* at the production input
location.   When less inventory is actually consumed (on the picking list journal),
it is important to revert the unconsumed inventory to a status of *On Order* so that
it can be returned to stock or used for other orders.   You revert this status by
reporting the last pallet for a production order, which also updates a checkbox
field (labeled Last Pallet) for a production order.

The "last pallet" transaction is only needed for scenarios with unconsumed
inventory at the production input location.   It is typically performed after
reporting all production activities.   The "last pallet" transaction serves no other
purpose.   It does not update production order status, so that an additional client
transaction may be needed to change status to *Reported as Finished*.   In addition,
other types of related transactions do not have the same impact as the "last pallet"
transaction, such as flagging a component as completely picked or changing
order status to *Reported as Finished.*

9.9 Life Cycles Related to Production Order Receiving

The basic process involves several related constructs, where the status for each
construct reflects various steps in the process.   Figure 9.6 summarizes this
information for the basic process, and shading highlights the key constructs
related to the Advanced WMS approach.   The major constructs include the use of
mobile devices for the reporting of a finished quantity and related putaway work,
with a status automatically updated by the different steps.

Reporting a finished quantity provides the starting point of the process, and
Figure 9.6 illustrates the steps associated with a reporting approach via mobile
devices.   Reporting a finished quantity via a mobile device will automatically
create and post a report as finished journal (termed an RAF journal for short),
which updates the item's inventory status to *Received*.   It can also automatically
create the putaway work for the finished quantity.

Figure 9.6   Life Cycles Related to the Basic Process
for Production Order Receiving

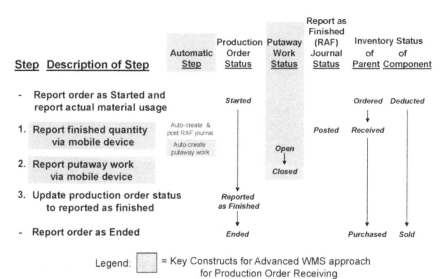

Step	Description of Step	Automatic Step	Production Order Status	Putaway Work Status	Report as Finished (RAF) Journal Status	Inventory Status of Parent	of Component
-	Report order as Started and report actual material usage		Started			Ordered	Deducted
1.	Report finished quantity via mobile device	Auto-create & post RAF journal / Auto-create putaway work		Open	Posted	Received	
2.	Report putaway work via mobile device			Closed			
3.	Update production order status to reported as finished		Reported as Finished				
-	Report order as Ended		Ended			Purchased	Sold

Legend: ☐ = Key Constructs for Advanced WMS approach
for Production Order Receiving

The figure includes the separate step for updating order status (via the client), which represents a required step when using mobile devices as the reporting approach for finished quantities. The right side of the figure illustrates the inventory status associated with the parent item and a component for the production order.

9.10 Reversing Transactions in Production Order Receiving

The ability to reverse transactions requires an understanding of the current point within the business process, and the associated status of key constructs. Borrowing from the previous figure, Figure 9.7 illustrates the steps within the basic process (shown in grey text) and the various points at which you can perform reversing transactions (shown in black text). The figure also illustrates the impact of a reversing transaction on status, and the arrows indicate the resulting point in the business process. As identified by step numbers in the figure, you can reverse transactions (1X) after initially creating the putaway work for a finished quantity and (AnyX) at any time prior to ending the production order.

Figure 9.7   Reversing Transactions in the Basic Process for Production Order Receiving

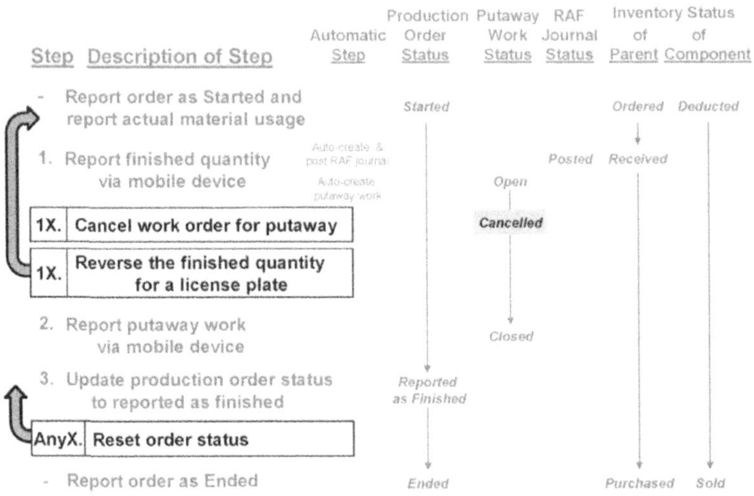

Step	Description of Step	Automatic Step	Production Order Status	Putaway Work Status	RAF Journal Status	Inventory Status of Parent	Inventory Status of Component
-	Report order as Started and report actual material usage		Started			Ordered	Deducted
1.	Report finished quantity via mobile device	Auto-create & post RAF journal Auto-create putaway work		Open	Posted	Received	
1X.	Cancel work order for putaway			Cancelled			
1X.	Reverse the finished quantity for a license plate						
2.	Report putaway work via mobile device			Closed			
3.	Update production order status to reported as finished		Reported as Finished				
AnyX.	Reset order status						
-	Report order as Ended		Ended			Purchased	Sold

Step 1X: Cancel Work Order for Putaway of Finished Quantity   You can cancel a work order prior to reporting any work, which changes the work order status to *Cancelled*. In this case, the finished quantity simply remains in the production output location, and you decide further steps such as moving or scrapping the inventory.

Step 1X: Reverse the Finished Quantity for a License Plate   You can reverse the finished quantity for a specified license plate by accessing the Reverse License Plate dialogue for a selected production order. The transaction will back out the item's inventory and the appropriate amount of raw materials will be placed back into the production input location. The arrow in Figure 9.7 indicates the impact of this reversing transaction, since you can start over with reporting actual material usage and finished quantities. The reversed quantity can reflect all or part of the license plate quantity. The transaction is typically performed when you over-report the finished quantity and need to make a correction.

Step AnyX: Reset Order Status for a Production Order   A production order can be reset to a previous status at any time prior to the *Ended* status. You indicate the desired order status on the reset order dialogue. The finished quantities will not be reversed by resetting the order status from *Reported as Finished to Started*. However, based on my testing, resetting to an earlier status typically encounters difficulties so that the order status cannot be changed.

9.11 Key Constructs for Production Order Receiving

The Advanced WMS approach for production order receiving involves several key constructs in addition to the production order. These include production output locations and setup information for several mobile device transactions.

Production Output Locations You identify a production output location when reporting the finished quantity for a production order (using either a mobile device or the client). It must be defined as an LP-controlled location to support automatic creation of putaway work. However, the mobile device transaction can be used to report both the finished quantity and putaway, where the putaway location does not need to be a license plate controlled location.

The production output location is normally inherited based on routing information about the resource performing the final operation, where you have assigned an output location to its resource group. This resource group (and a resource) is determined by scheduling logic for the operation's resource requirements. The inherited value can be overridden when reporting the finished quantity.

Mobile Device Transactions Several mobile device transactions apply to production order receiving. The primary transactions include reporting the finished quantity for a production order and the related putaway, and a combination of these two steps. With each variation, you start by entering the production order number when reporting the receipt.

◆ *Menu Item for Reporting Finished Quantity* As part of defining the menu item, you select a work creation process for *report as finished*. The receipt must be placed in an LP-controlled location and assigned a license plate number. Completing the transaction will automatically create putaway work for the license plate. You can review this putaway work by accessing it for the related production order (on the Production Order form), for a selected work order (on the All Work form).

◆ *Menu Item for Putaway of a Finished Quantity* As part of defining the menu item, you select the policy for *use existing work* and the work class for *finished goods putaway*. A work template and a location directive are also defined for the work type of *finished goods putaway*.

◆ *Menu Item for Reporting Finished Quantity and Putaway*   As part of defining the menu item, you select a work creation process for *report as finished and putaway*. A work template and a location directive are also defined for the work type of *finished goods putaway*.

Another mobile device transaction involves reporting the last pallet received, which was explained as an additional step in the basic process (Section 9.7).

9.12 Major Variations of Production Order Receiving

The basic process for production order receiving provides the baseline for explaining key considerations and major variations. Many of these were covered in a previous chapter (Sections 7.5 and 7.6), such as the significance of a single order and production inspection. Two additional variations involve serialized and batch-controlled material.

Receive Batch-Controlled Items The assignment of a batch number to a finished quantity reflects several policies such as manual versus automatic assignment. The system supports automatic and manual assignment of a batch number in transactions reported via the client. Automatic assignment is also supported by mobile device transactions, but manual assignment requires an additional policy (labeled "override batch number") in the definition of the mobile device menu item.

Receive Serialized Items The assignment of serial numbers to a finished quantity reflects several policies such as manual versus automatic assignment. The system supports automatic and manual assignment of a serial number in transactions reported via the client. Automatic assignment is also supported by mobile device transactions, but manual assignment is not supported.

9.13 Additional Case Studies

Case 9.1:   Wave Picking for Production The warehouse planner typically created a production wave on a daily basis, and selectively added the components of released orders to the wave lines. The wave would then be released in order to create work orders for raw material picking, and warehouse workers would deliver the picked material to the desired production input locations. The picking work identified the desired pick and put locations.

Case 9.2:   Putaway of Finished Goods after Production A machine operator reported finished quantities into a production output location (with license plate identifiers for each pallet). This created work orders for directed putaway, and warehouse workers would then report the putaway into stocking locations.

9.14 Executive Summary

The Advanced WMS approach supports multiple variations in picking and receiving material for production orders. As a starting point, a simple production scenario for internal manufacturing provided the context for explaining the basic processes for picking and receiving. Given this context, the chapter described a simple yet typical business process for production order picking and for reporting finished quantities. For each process, the chapter explained the related life cycles, reversing transactions, key constructs and major variations.

Chapter 10

Quality Considerations for Manufactured Items

The concerns of quality management typically extend across every aspect of supply chain management. This broad viewpoint ranges from the definition of item and product structure information through sourcing purchased material, actual production, sales shipments, and returns. A narrower viewpoint focuses on several aspects of unique functionality for quality management.

Some aspects of a narrow viewpoint have been covered elsewhere -- such as using cases for quality purposes and inventory blocking approaches – so they are not repeated here.[1] One of the blocking approaches involves quality orders. This section provides further explanation of quality orders for production, and summarizes several variations of production inspection. These topics are reflected in the following sections within the chapter.

1. Quality Orders for Production Purposes
2. Variations of Production Inspection

10.1 Quality Orders for Production Purposes

Product testing entails the use of quality orders to report test results against a group of predefined tests. The explanation of quality orders can be segmented into three areas: the definition of tests and test groups, the use of quality orders for reporting test results, and the rules for automatic generation of quality orders. This explanation only focuses on the rules for automatic generation related to production, and the related use of a quality order.

---

[1] These topics were covered in the prerequisite reading of the "Essential Guide for Supply Chain Management", and in the complete book.

Rules for Automatic Generation of a Quality Order You can define rules (termed *quality association records*) for automatic generation of a quality order in different business processes. Each rule defines the set of tests, the acceptable quality level (AQL), and the sampling plan that apply to the automatically generated quality orders. Each rule also defines the event and conditions for automatically generating a quality order within a business process for the item. This section focuses on the production process, and the rules are summarized in Figure 10.1 and described below.

Figure 10.1 Rules for Automatic Generation of a Quality Order Related to Production

Business Process	Label of the event that triggers a quality order		The actual event that triggers a quality order	Conditions			Destructive Test Allowed
Reference Type	Execution	Document		Site	Item	Other	
Production Order	**Before report as finished**		Initial attempt to report a finished quantity	Site-specific or company-wide	Item-specific, all items, or quality group-specific	N/A	No
	After report as finished		After reporting a finished quantity for a production order				Yes
Route operation	**Before report as finished**		Initially create a production order			Resource or Group Master Operation or Route Group	No
	After report as finished		Report the operation as finished				

The figure summarizes the events and conditions for generating a quality order related to a production order, either for a production operation or when reporting a finished quantity. These two types of events are expressed in terms of the relevant document and execution timing. The figure also identifies the actual event that triggers automatic generation of a quality order.

♦ *Production Order Process.* The generation of a quality order can occur before or after reporting a finished quantity. A quality order that requires destructive testing can only be generated after reporting a finished quantity. The need for a quality order can reflect a particular site or item, or a combination of these conditions.

♦ *Route Operation for a Production Order* When a production order contains a routing operation, the quality order can be generated before or after reporting the operation as finished. The need for a quality order can reflect a particular site, item or quality group, or a combination of these conditions. The need for a quality order can also reflect a specific master operation or the route group assigned to operations.

A rule must be defined for each variation in a business process requiring automatic creation of a quality order. For example, the required tests may vary by item, so that a rule must be defined for each item. The validity dates for a quality association record enable you to model planned changes in the testing requirements.

Use of a Quality Order   A quality order defines the tests that need to be performed for a manufactured item, either for a production operation or a finished quantity. In addition to communicating the need to perform tests, it provides a mechanism for reporting results against the tests. As noted on the previous point, you can establish quality guidelines for automatically creating a quality order. You can also manually create a quality order.

After reporting the test results for every test within a quality order, you initiate a validation process that assigns a pass or fail status (based on meeting the overall AQL) and closes the quality order. When you try performing the next step in the business process, a message warns you when the quality order has failed or has not yet been closed. In addition, you can optionally reopen the quality order and force the validation process to assign a pass status by accepting any error conditions.

You can optionally generate a certificate of analysis that displays the test results for a quality order. For example, a certificate of analysis could be printed for a batch of material being shipped to a customer. The printed test results will only be displayed for designated tests within the quality order.

When using batch attributes for a batch-controlled item, the test results for a quantitative test on a quality order can optionally update the associated batch attribute. This requires a mapping between the test and its associated batch attribute.

You can optionally create a nonconformance report when a quality order identifies defective material. The nonconformance report provides the basis for further investigation.

10.2 Variations of Production Inspection

There are many variations of modeling production inspection for manufactured items.   For example, production inspection may be reported by a machine operator at the time of reporting the finished quantity of a production order, or reported afterward by a quality control clerk using an automatically-created quality order.   The test results for a quality order may be reported for a small sample while the material remains at a production output location, or a finished quantity may be placed in a separate QC area until test results have been reported.   Validation failure of the test results can automatically update the Inventory Status of the finished quantity, such as changing status to a value of *To-Be-Scrapped* or *Needs-Rework.*   It can also update the batch disposition code for a batch-controlled item.

As an explanatory approach, the different approaches for production inspection are more easily explained via case studies.   A common scenario involves reporting by a quality control clerk using quality orders and Inventory Status (Case 10.1).   Another common scenario involves reporting by the machine operator (Case 10.2). Additional case studies illustrate some other approaches to production inspection.

10.3 Additional Case Studies

Case 10.1: Production Inspection using Quality Orders and Inventory Status The warehouse manager and quality control (QC) manager at a manufacturing company were considering options for using automatically-generated quality orders for finished quantities of production orders. One option involved the use of Inventory Status, where the quality order would automatically change the value based on pass/fail validation. Passing the validation changed the value to *Good.* Failing the validation changed the value to *To-Be-Scrapped* or *Needs-Rework*, as defined by the quality control clerk performing the quality order. The proposed business process is illustrated in Figure 10.2 and described below.

The production inspection process starts with reporting a finished quantity into a production location which automatically generates a quality order. The process has multiple end points reflecting the test results of the quality order.   The inventory remains in the production location until completion of the quality order. The process consists of several steps performed by different roles, and three of these steps merit further explanation.

Figure 10.2 Typical Process for Production Inspection
Using a Quality Order

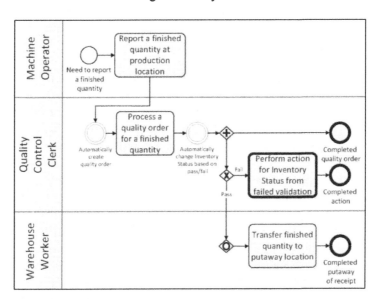

♦ *Process a Quality Order for a Finished Quantity.* The activities of quality control clerks are coordinated based on a review of open quality orders, using either the Quality Orders form or the Inventory Blocking form. When reporting test results for a given quality order, the quality control clerk indicates the applicable Inventory Status for validation failure, such as *To-Be-Scrapped* or *Needs- Rework.* Validation automatically updates the Inventory Status.

If applicable, the quality control clerk creates a nonconformance related to problems with the item or production order, and/or creates a case about the problem.

♦ *Perform Action for Inventory Status from failed Validation.* The quality control clerk reports an inventory adjustment for material assigned an Inventory Status of *To-Be-Scrapped.* The production planner creates a rework order for material with a *Needs-Rework* status. For material with a *Good* status, the warehouse worker can report a transfer from the production location to a stocking location.

Case 10.2:   Production Inspection by Machine Operators   The production manager wanted the machine operators to report inspection of finished quantities for production orders. A machine operator could immediately report a trashed quantity (aka the error quantity) when using the Reported as

Finished form, thereby bypassing the need for additional steps. Alternatively, the machine operator could assign an inventory status of *To-Be-Scrapped*, *Needs-Rework* or *Needs-Inspection* to a finished quantity, thereby indicating the need for an additional step.   The corresponding steps involved an inventory adjustment, a rework order, or a quality order.

Case 10.3: Quality Orders during the Production Process The quality manager wanted to obtain test results during the production process for a manufactured item.   The item's routing information identified multiple operations with operation numbers (such as 10, 20, 30 and 40), and the test results were needed at selected operation numbers (such as 20 and 30). These testing requirements were defined as part of a Quality Association for the item and each selected operation number, which would trigger automatic creation of a quality order after the operation was reported as finished.

Case 10.4: Routing Operation for Production Inspection A separate operation for production inspection was defined in the route version for manufactured items because it required significance time by quality control clerks. The operation identified the resource requirements for a resource group that represented the various clerks. A quality order was also created for the operation so that test results could be recorded.

Case 10.5: Certificates of Analysis for Sales Order Shipments A manufacturer enclosed a certificate of analysis with sales order shipments of selected items. The certificate reflected the test results reported for the item, where test results were captured as part of a quality order. The contents of a certificate of analysis reflected each customer's requirements for selected test results.

10.4 Executive Summary

This chapter summarized two quality considerations for production.   One involved the use of quality orders to identify needed tests and capture test results. The other involved variations of production inspection and related case studies.

Chapter 11

Summary

This book focused on how Microsoft Dynamics AX provides an integrated ERP system to support supply chain management in discrete manufacturing. The targeted reader consists of SCM professionals that need to initially learn AX for manufacturing. It provided an overview of the essential business processes and capabilities, and presented a linear sequence of topics that build on each other. It covered the embedded conceptual models and business processes that ultimately shape your vocabulary for describing system usage.

The linear sequence of topics started with the definition of a manufactured item, which included the item's coverage planning data and the policies for serialized or batch-controlled material. The sequence continued with the definition of bills of material and routing information, the calculation of product costs, the common S&OP scenarios, and the use of master scheduling logic to coordinate supply chain activities. Subsequent chapters covered production order processing, and the two major options of a basic and advanced approach to warehouse management for production order picking/receiving. Several quality considerations were also covered. Many of the chapters included Business Process Modeling (BPM) diagrams about basic business processes, and these provided the foundation for covering major variations. Case studies illustrated how the AX software functionality applies to many different scenarios in discrete manufacturing.

The book represents one of a series of Essential Guides, and a previously published guide (about SCM) should be considered prerequisite reading. As an Essential Guide, this book represents an abbreviated version of my complete book for "Supply Chain Management using Microsoft Dynamics AX: 2016 Edition". The two chapters about warehouse management for production orders represent an abbreviated version of my complete book for "Warehouse Management using Microsoft Dynamics AX: 2016 Edition".

The book contents covered the two major options currently available for using AX, which can be labeled "Dynamics AX 2012 R3" and the "new Dynamics AX". The two options provide the same supply chain management functionality with some slight differences, so that the book contents apply to both options. The book identified the slight differences such as the variations in user experience and the workspace capabilities.

Concluding Remarks When learning any ERP software package, it is important to understand its underlying conceptual models and how it supports basic business processes and their variations. It is easy to get bogged down in the navigational details. This book summarized how Microsoft Dynamics AX can support supply chain management in discrete manufacturing businesses, and addressed the learning objectives for those new to AX.

Appendix A

Appendix A
Scope of Book Topics
and Prior Research

The book focuses on supply chain management topics for discrete manufacturing companies, and this focus guided the prior research and the scope of book topics.

Prior Research Several steps of prior research were undertaken to understand the supply chain management requirements in discrete manufacturing, and the AX functionality to support those requirements. With respect to AX 2012 R3 (as well as previous AX versions), these steps included participation in training classes, webinars, and conference sessions; reviews of the existing training materials, e-learning lessons, user documentation and sales demo materials; reviews of blogs and articles; discussions with users, development personnel, and field consultants; and hands-on testing for thousands of use cases that reflected common requirements in discrete manufacturing. With few exceptions, only those capabilities personally tested and proven were included in the book contents.[1] The same approach was also undertaken for my previous books about Dynamics AX. The discussions with experienced field consultants helped identify the dominant business practices at current users. On-going opportunities to consult with current users have supplemented this understanding.

The prior research concerning the new Dynamics AX has been following similar steps. This included participation in pre-release webinars and conferences, discussions with leading experts and Microsoft team members, reading the currently available information, and hands-on testing of hundreds of use cases. These same use cases were previously tested for AX 2012 R3, thereby supporting a comparative analysis of the two options. The book contents reflect my prior research up until the beginning of the year 2016.

---

[1] The prior research and hands-on testing for AX 2012 R3 reflect the software capabilities through the CU9 release.

The prior research about SCM requirements included my consulting and teaching experiences with discrete manufacturing firms across the past three decades. These experiences included responses to numerous RFPs (requests for proposal) for an ERP system, face-to-face consulting engagements with several hundred firms, and teaching executive seminars, APICS certification classes, MBA courses, and user group sessions. My understanding is continually being supplemented by staying abreast of the current literature and discussions with various thought leaders about using ERP systems in discrete manufacturing.

Scope of Book Topics   The book topics focus on the manufacturing-related capabilities for supply chain management, and the selection of book topics was shaped by several factors. First, the selected topics excluded the integrated accounting applications -- such as payables, receivables, general ledger, payroll and human resources -- except for key intersection points with SCM. Second, several SCM-related topics were excluded because of book length considerations -- such as lean manufacturing and project-oriented manufacturing – although they are mentioned in several places. Each of these excluded topics merit a separate book, much like my separate books about warehouse management and process manufacturing. The excluded topic of non-stock purchases reflects the focus on material items. Third, a few topics were excluded because they could not be personally tested and proven within the budgeted time.

The book length considerations precluded screen shots.[2] Other important topics of system development and usage were also excluded, such as business intelligence, security, and customization capabilities within the AX development environment.

Contributions to the AX Body of Knowledge   The body of knowledge related to Microsoft Dynamics AX consists of several levels and components. The foundation level consists of the software, documentation and training materials provided by Microsoft. Additional contributions to the AX body of knowledge build on this foundation. In terms of the book's contributions, I have attempted to summarize the relevant information with an integrative viewpoint of how the whole system fits together to support supply chain management in discrete manufacturing businesses. The book explains the embedded conceptual models and business processes for running these businesses.

---

[2] One argument against screen shot examples is that many companies tailor the standard screens, and the displayed information is also affected by license key activation. .

List of Figures

List of Cases

About the Author

Scott Hamilton has specialized in SCM/ERP information systems for three decades and consulted globally with several hundred manufacturing/distribution companies. His publications include multiple books about SCM using Dynamics AX as well as two textbooks about SCM/ERP, and his books have been translated into Russian and Chinese. His regular column "The AX Solution Architect" is published in MSDynamicsWorld.com. Scott has been a frequent speaker at Microsoft and AXUG events around the world, and a multi-year winner of the rarely-given Microsoft MVP award for AX. He earned a doctorate in information systems specializing in manufacturing and taught SCM/ERP as an MBA professor at several leading universities in North America, Europe and the Pacific Rim. He lives in Minnesota, a place where people still build ice castles.

About UXC Eclipse

Scott Hamilton has become the "go to" authority on Microsoft Dynamics AX in the manufacturing space. His books provide valuable insights into the market place we serve, which gives us all the opportunity to expand our thinking and see beyond the software features and functions.

UXC Eclipse is widely recognized as a global leader in industry solutions built on the Dynamics AX platform. We have a depth of experience across the horizontal global ERP market with specific focus on industry solutions for Retail, Wholesale and Distribution, Manufacturing and the surrounding supply chain.

We help organizations streamline their business and operational processes to bring the best from their organizational experience to the best of our Dynamics AX solutions; the result is 'win-win'. From their Dynamics AX solutions, our customers realize operational efficiencies, improve business performance and heighten their supply chain collaboration. At UXC Eclipse we use a combination of old-fashioned service with ISO-9001 accredited quality systems and controls to ensure our implementations deliver to our customers' expectations – on time and on budget. Our happy customers are the true indication of our success. With a global team of over 650 people, some 2,700 customer sites rely on UXC Eclipse for their project implementation services and everyday support.

We trust you find this book to be a useful insight into Microsoft Dynamics AX. If UXC Eclipse can be of service on your supply chain journey, then please get in touch with us at *www.uxceclipse.com*

Bradley Stroop
Chief Executive Officer
UXC Eclipse Group

Made in the USA
Monee, IL
05 October 2020